THE RAILWAY PUZZLE BOOK

Will Adams

THE RAILWAY PUZZLE BOOK

Will Adams

Patrick Stephens Limited

INTRODUCTION

Special thanks to Geoff Body
for his help in checking
the proofs.

First published in 1989

British Library Cataloguing in Publication Data

Adams, Will
    The railway puzzle book.
    1. Pictorial puzzles. Special subjects: Transport
    I. Title
    793.73

ISBN 1-85260-187-6

Patrick Stephens Limited is part of the
Thorsons Publishing Group, Wellingborough,
Northamptonshire NN8 2RQ, England.

Typeset by Harper Phototypesetters Limited,
Northampton, England.

Printed in Great Britain by MacKays of Letchworth

10 9 8 7 6 5 4 3 2 1

Of course, I blame my parents.

It was they who gave me a grubby little
notebook and a stubby little pencil. It was they
who took me, a tiny, defenceless, tubby little
boy in shorts and wellies, a mere babe, into the
depths of the Warwickshire countryside. It was
they who set me down beside the Trent Valley
line between Rugby and Nuneaton where a
footbridge spanned the tracks, and left me to
myself for a whole, endless summer's
afternoon.
    Did they realise the risks they were taking?
What on earth did they expect? When I'd seen
my first 'Royal Scot' spinning southwards
between the hawthorn hedges on that magical
silver highway, witnessed my first thumping,
swaying, squealing, creaking, loose-coupled
mixed goods in the charge of an '8F' or 'Black
Five', did they think that I'd just turn round
and go play football with the other lads?
    If so, they were to be sadly disappointed. I
was hooked. I was lost. I had experienced the
irresistible sight and sensation of those
beckoning, seemingly infinite silver lines
disappearing over the horizon like a flat
shimmering rainbow. And in those days of the
late '50s and early '60s, the crocks of gold still
on offer included steam sheds, mechanical
signal boxes, maroon-liveried compartment
coaches with dusty upholstery, rail joints, brake
vans, shunting . . .
    And so it went on. One thing led to another.
The school Railway Society took me to places
undreamed of. Speke. Goole. Canton. Row
upon row of silent, sighing, dripping steam
locomotives towering in immeasurable
splendour above the shoulders of us scribbling
kids, and eliciting no less a feeling of awe and
excitement than was felt by the discoverers of
the Valley of the Kings or the Chinese
terracotta army.
    Then, as my appetite for engine numbers at
last began to wane, so I discovered railway
history and railway operation. And railway
relics. Trespass signs. Waybills, handbills.
Signalling equipment. Nameboards. Girls. Oh
yes, girls were also now taking up some of my

attention along with other sundry distractions. One such, you will not be surprised to learn, was a mania for solving, then compiling, puzzles.

So I got married. Got a tandem. Got a mortgage. Got a car. Got a daughter. Two daughters. Two dogs, two rabbits. But still the fascination with everything railway persisted.

Then, last year, someone said 'How about a railway puzzle book?' I thought it over seriously, but before they'd said 'book' I'd said 'Yes'. So here I am combining two of the loves of my life while another love of my life sits in the other room watching some old movie (one of the loves of her life) and the two little loves of both our lives are asleep (I hope) upstairs. And now that the introduction part of the Introduction is over, let's turn to the puzzles.

The first and most important thing to say is that you don't have to be good at puzzles to solve them — there are no anagrams, cryptic clues, brainteasers. You just have to know something about Britain's railways and their history (or at least have a few books you can look the answers up in if you get stuck). Furthermore, this book is not an attempt to prove how much I know about railways, or for that matter how much you already know. Anyone who already knows the answers to every clue and question is not going to get much fun out of it.

In many ways it's quite a personal book. Although I've tried to include a wide variety of subjects, any biases in certain directions are mine, as are all the photographs, which allowed me to take a very pleasant excursion down the Memory Lane branch. And the amount of pleasure I've derived from compiling the puzzles has been at least matched by the satisfaction I've gained from learning so much more about our railways, mechanically, geographically and historically. I very much hope that it works that way for you too. I hope that it sends you searching for your old Ian Allan *ABC* or *Observer's Book of Steam Locomotives*. I hope that you have to search through a few old railway books, atlases,

gazetteers and timetables (I did!). I hope that even if you don't know an answer, you'll have some fun looking it up or hazarding a guess, as well as learning a little bit of railway trivia.

And trivia is an important concept here. This is not a book for the rivet-counters, for the people who can tell you the driving wheel diameter of the North Eastern's 'S3' Class without looking it up (it was 5′8″, by the way — I just looked it up). This book is much more for the general enthusiast who like me is interested to know why there were water troughs *inside* Standedge tunnel, or what Troy, Defiance and Legacy have in common, or why a record player was installed on a Leeds express in the 1930s (answers at the back . . .).

And one final note — I generally refer to places, locomotives, etc in the present tense even if they are long since gone, and relate them to their pre-Grouping ownership. So a clue such as 'LNWR station and junction between A and B' doesn't mean that the station is still to be found between A and B and is still in operation, and isn't meant to imply that it didn't subsequently make it into LMS or even BR ownership. And since the railway scene is constantly changing, questions or clues relating to recent events are correct at the time of writing (early 1989).

So please enjoy the puzzles, and if you get stuck or frustrated with them, don't blame me. As I said at the beginning, blame my parents. Blame my fellow childhood trainspotters. Blame Steve, with whom I walked many a mile of disused railway line. Blame my wife, Tricia, who happily shares my interest in railways (well, up to a point . . .). Blame anyone who ever wrote a decent railway book or captured a pulse-quickening moment on camera. Blame PSL for publishing such first-rate railway books. Because all these people are morally responsible for aiding and abetting my passion for railways. And it is to them that this book is dedicated, with deep gratitude.

Will Adams
Denford, Northants

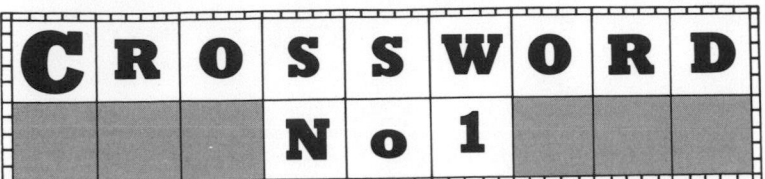

Across

1 BR engineer responsible for the Standard steam locos of the 1950s (7)

5 Standard is 4′8½″ (5)

10 21 Down of the LMS, 1945-7 (5)

11 The 'Cheltenham ——', the world's fastest train in the '20s (5)

12 —— *Grange* (6857) or —— *Minstrel* (60528) (5)

13 Famous Leeds locomotive manufacturers (7)

14 Class of noblemen after which Nos 5043-5063 were named (5)

15 On a steam locomotive it may couple or connect (3)

17 Town connected to Manifold by light railway (4)

19 One of the antelopes after which the 'B1's were named (3)

20 *Harrow* and *Cheltenham* belonged to this class (7)

24 Number of 'Deltics' (excluding the prototype) now in preservation (3)

25 GWR class of 4-6-0s from which the 'Castle' Class developed (4)

26 Monosyllabic LNWR station between Whitchurch and Shrewsbury (3)

29 Nickname for a signalman, from the days when they were policemen (5)

30 The 'E' of 'GER' (7)

32 'Britannia' '23' (5)

33 Number of cylinders on *Flying Scotsman* (5)

34 Once on the Princes Risborough-Oxford line, this Bucks town is now a freight terminus (5)

35 All signalmen can talk on this 'omnibus'! (5)

36 American-sounding nickname for the Highland Railway 4-4-0 tank locomotives (7)

Down

1 Location of the famous locomotive trials in 1829 (8)

2 Nickname of the Waterloo & City underground railway (5)

3 Descriptive of Kimble on the GW & GC, Somerford on the GWR and Steeping on the GNR (6)

4 The 'S' of 'LMS' (8)

6 'Great' name for 'Britannia' '9' (6)

7 General Manager of the Midland Railway, 1906-18 (3,6)

8 —— *Dempster Lines*, 'Merchant Navy' No 35030 (5)

9 Those of the Bricklayers provided the original London terminus of the SER (4)

16 Essential substance for a steam locomotive driver! (3)

18 City whose principal MPD was Haymarket (9)

21 Initials by which a railway's locomotive superintendent is sometimes known (1,1,1)

22 Headquarters of the Cambrian Railways (8)

23 *The —— Royal*, the LMS's first 'Pacific' (8)

26 Heraldic creature, symbol of the Midland Railway (6)

27 Type of building after which Nos 7800-29 were named (5)

28 It's in Makerfield on the GCR but under Hill on the Midland (6)

29 City (not London) containing a Green Park station (4)

31 Midland station just east of Cowburn Tunnel on the Hope Valley line (5)

WESTERN ENTERPRISE

. . . was the name of D1000, the first of the much-loved Type 4 locomotives.
Below are 39 more 'Western' names to be fitted into the grid according to
their length. To start you off are the names of four sheds to which **these**
locomotives were allocated during their careers.

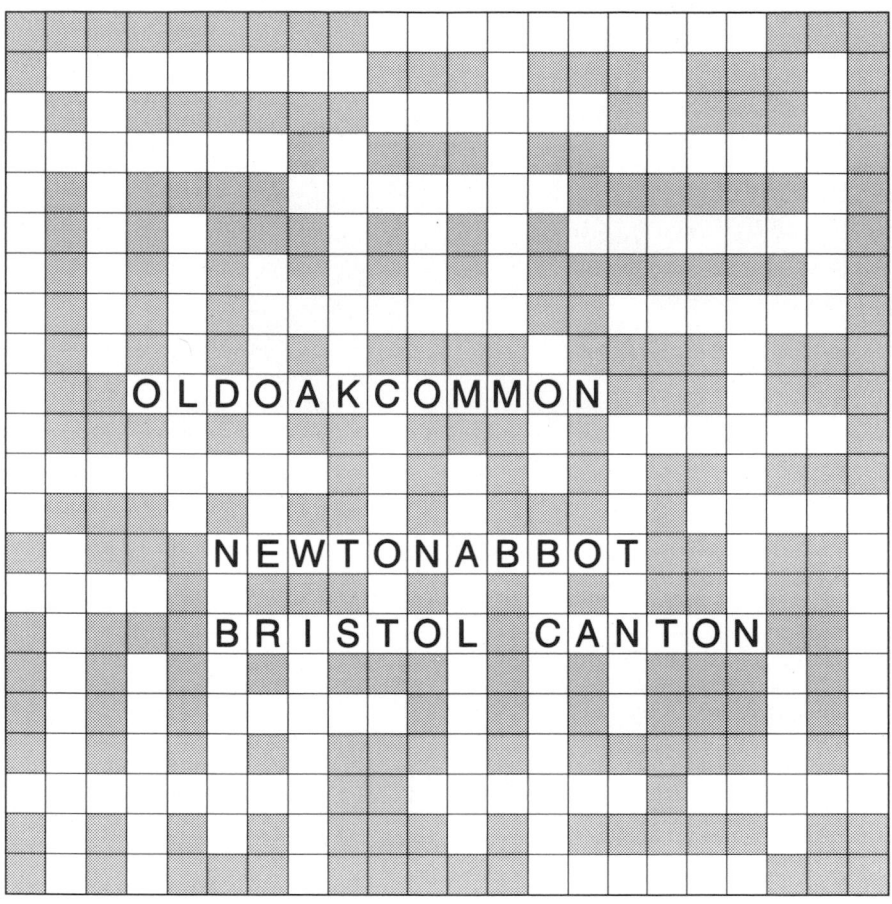

4	Duke	6	Lancer	7	Bulwark	8	Advocate	9	Buccaneer
	Hero		Prince		Consort		Cavalier		Centurion
	King		Ranger		Dragoon		Dominion		Firebrand
	Lord		Regent		Duchess		Explorer		
			Renown		Emperor		Huntsman	10	Challenger
5	Druid		Sultan		Invader		Nobleman		Pathfinder
	Envoy		Yeoman		Monitor		Reliance		
	Queen				Prefect		Rifleman	11	Legionnaire
	Ruler						Sentinel		
							Vanguard		

PICTURE THE SCENE
EXETER ST DAVIDS

Talking of 'Westerns', here's a picture I took at Exeter St Davids in April 1976.

1 What relatively unusual form of transmission did the 'Westerns' have?

2 The 'Westerns' had all been withdrawn a year after this picture was taken — but in what year were they introduced?

3 What is the significance of the letter 'M' on the signal arm above the locomotive's cab?

4 What is the function of the small signal arm with the horizontal white stripe placed below the arm that is 'off'?

5 The signal box in the middle distance controlled the junction of two lines. The line curving away to the left climbs a notoriously steep bank to Exeter Central. What is the gradient?

6 What was the name of the signal box (which has since been removed for preservation)?

7 Exeter Central had a different name prior to 1933. What was it?

8 A new signal centre opened at Exeter in April 1988. It replaces 31 mechanical signalboxes from Athelney in the east to where on the main line to the west?

9 Which Exeter station is the next station along the main line to the west?

10 Exeter was originally a 'broad gauge' station. What was the width of the broad gauge?

Across

3 Device carried by the driver of a train to permit safe occupation of a single line section (5)

5 Major junction where the North and South signal boxes were fitted with two-tier miniature all-electric frames by the LNWR (5)

7 Name often given to a modern power signal box (5)

8 Signal equipment manufacturer famous for the electrical tablet method of operating single lines (4)

9 Name given to the structure which contains the levers and locking in a 10 down signal box (5)

11 See 25 down

12 '—— and block', famous signalling system invented by W. R. Sykes (4)

13 Type of signal normally placed on the approach side of a signal box (4)

14 Colour of the lowest aspect of a 28 down aspect signal (3)

15 Device sometimes installed beyond trap points at the end of a loop or siding to arrest runaways (4,4)

17 Warning signal (7)

18 Widespread signalling method whereby the line is divided into sections in which there can only be one train at a time (5,6)

20 Name usually applied to one who installs or maintains signalling systems (6)

21 Instruments providing continuous box-to-box advice of approaching traffic, its type and route, used in intensively worked areas (5,10)

22 This might be indicated mechanically below a signal arm, or by a 'theatre'-type indicator on an electric signal (5)

23 Electro-mechanical system of cab signalling . . . (1,1,1)

25 . . . pioneered by this company in the 1930s . . . (1,1,1)

26 . . . and its post-Nationalization BR equivalent (1,1,1)

27 Word used to describe a signal in the clear position (3)

29 Abbreviation for a set of signals situated between signal boxes to shorten sections (1,1,1)

30 City where the Midland Railway's signal works was situated (5)

31 LNWR station where a 44-arm duplicated gantry, the '—— Bedstead', had to be erected when the GCR girder bridge was built behind the original in the 1890s (5)

Down

1 The first word of 29 across (12)

2 Type of colour light signal with a single lens and a moving vane of coloured roundels (11)

4 Devices of which 'peggers' and 'non-peggers' are the principal varieties (5,11)

6 Type of signal with a moving arm . . . (9)

10 . . . usually worked under this kind of signalling system (10)

16 Safety device ensuring that points are fully 'home' before corresponding signals can be cleared (8)

19 Station which was once famously worked by four signal boxes with a total of 391 levers (4)

24 Signal controlling the entry into the section in advance (8)

25 and 11 across Low, round-faced shunting signal (6,4)

28 Number of aspects of the type of signals capable of displaying a 'double yellow' (4)

GANTRY

Alas, the gantry opposite and many others like it up and down the country are rapidly becoming a thing of the past. All the clues in this 'signal gantry' crossword are connected with signalling.

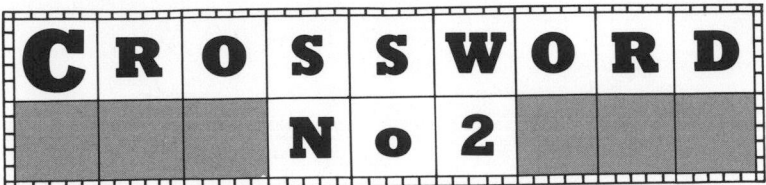

Across

1 Loughborough diesel manufacturers responsible for several BR classes (5)

6 *St Paddy* was one, as was *Tulyar* . . . (9)

8 . . . and their engines were supplied by this manufacturer (6)

10 East Coast Main Line station famous for its level crossing (7)

11 Historic former Liverpool station on the L&MR near the famous Moorish Arch (4,4)

12 D803, and an LNWR station near West Bromwich (appropriately!) (6)

16 Signalmen's slang for a signal (3)

18 'The —— City', Glasgow-Aberdeen 21 down (7)

19 Co Durham steelmaking town, destination of iron ore trains from Tyne Dock (7)

20 Pre-Grouping company which had the third largest network after the GWR and LNWR (1,1,1)

22 Type of carriage increasingly rare on BR, and completely disappeared on London Transport! (6)

27 L&MR station at which William Huskisson was run down on the opening day in 1830 (8)

28 Description of the Britannia Bridge across the Menai Strait (7)

30 Material much used for chimney-capping on steam locomotives! (6)

31 City containing the headquarters of the Highland Railway (9)

32 What the fireman did to reach the headquarters of the North Staffordshire Railway? (5)

Down

1 Engine assisting a train in the rear (6)

2 GWR Cornwall terminus, or GER Huntingdonshire junction (2,4)

3 Designer of the Festiniog Railway 0-4-4-0 bogie steam locomotive (7)

4 'Big ——', nickname of the MR 0-10-0 Lickey 1 down (6)

5 Code for a diesel or electric locomotive with two driven axles only on each bogie (2-2)

7 LSWR Devon terminus after which 'West Country' No 34010 was named (8)

9 It might be fish-bellied or bull-head (4)

13 Working grouping of locomotivemen (4)

14 Nineteenth-century inventor who patented a steam locomotive with a deliberately low centre of gravity (8)

15 Street giving its name to the LNWR's Liverpool station (4)

16 Yeovil —— Mill (3)

17 Company whose London Extension was opened in 1899 (1,1,1)

21 The 'Pines ——' (7)

23 What 'Warship' D839 was not prepared to do, apparently! (6)

24 Railway enthusiast and photographer Canon Treacy's first name (4)

25 Receptacle once provided between the rails at locomotive sheds (6)

26 First name of the GWR's Mr Churchward (6)

29 —— Moor Tunnel, landmark on the Settle & Carlisle line (4)

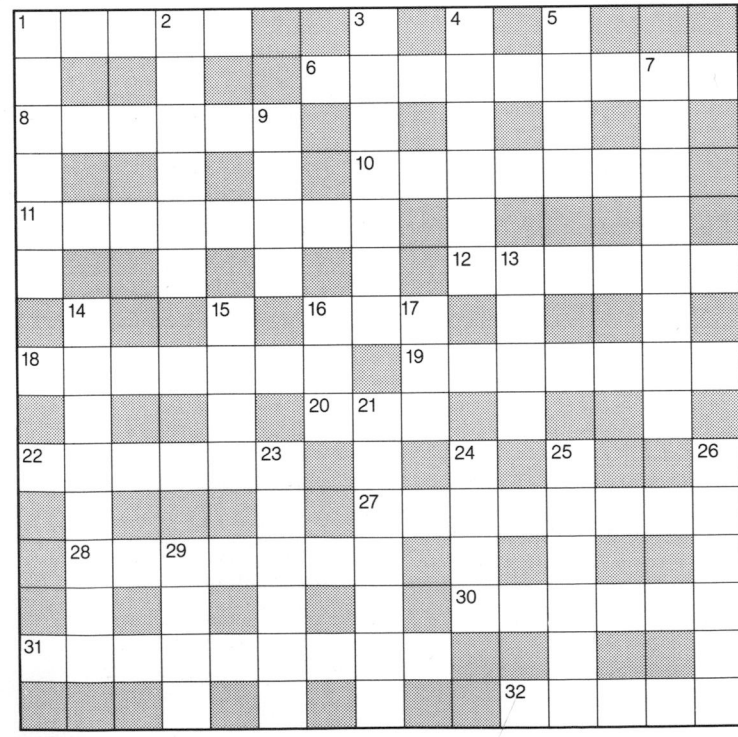

The grid represents a stretch of quadruple-track main line, two up lines and two down lines, linked by some intensive pointwork. The answers to the clues are all place-names with railway connections — fit each into the boxes starting at the numbered square and reading in the direction stated. Some letters are shared by two or more answers. One answer has been inserted to show you how it works.

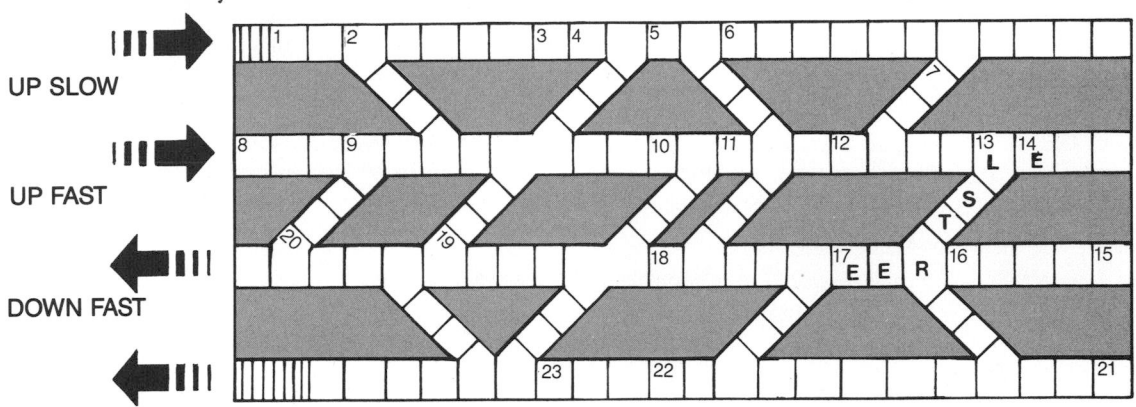

UP SLOW

UP FAST

DOWN FAST

DOWN SLOW

Clues

1 Up slow-up fast
Rutland town on the Midland Railway between Corby and Melton Mowbray (6)

2 Up slow
Junction south of Banbury for the Kingham and Oxford lines (5,6)

3 Up slow
M&GN junction of the Peterborough and Spalding lines (6,6)

4 Up slow-up fast
North Staffordshire Railway junction town (8)

5 Up slow
Junction on the Redhill-Ashford SE&CR main line (9)

6 Up slow-down fast
Midlands city boasting Arkwright Street and London Road stations (10)

7 Up fast-up slow
'Oriental' London location with two stations (6)

8 Up fast
Plymouth junction and MPD (5)

9 Up fast
Channel port with Town and Harbour stations (6)

10 Up fast
St Davids, or Central? (6)

11 Up fast-down slow
End of the branch line from 10 Central (7)

12 Up fast
River valley used by the southern part of the Settle & Carlisle line (6)

12 Up fast-up slow
Derbyshire town containing Butterley, HQ of the Midland Railway Centre (6)

12 Up fast-down fast
East Coast Main Line junction and level crossing (7)

13 Up fast
Staffordshire town linked to Manifold (4)

14 Up fast-down fast
Herts town linked with Borehamwood on the Midland main line (7)

15 Down fast
Herts station and famous cutting on the London & Birmingham main line (5)

16 Down fast
Outer London station on the GWR's High Wycombe line, junction for Ealing (9)

17 Down fast-down slow
North London borough — 'Lock' or 'Town' on the GER, 'Chase' on the GNR (7)

18 Down fast
County city on the East Coast Main Line (6)

19 Down fast
—— Dale, scenic location on the Midland main line in the Peak District (6)

20 Down fast-up fast
Station and water-troughs on the North Wales main line (4)

21 Down slow
Devon town formerly linked with Lynton (10)

21 Down slow-down fast
Midland junction at the top of the Licky Incline (5,5)

22 Down slow-down fast
Bank Top, or North Road? (10)

23 Down slow
County city with Midland, GCR, GNR and GER facilities (7)

TITLED TRAINS

1 The LNWR ran its 'Irish Mail' from Euston to Holyhead, the GWR from Paddington to — where?

2 Which Irish Sea port was the northern destination of the 'Ulster Express' until its withdrawal in 1975?

3 Which city gives its nickname to the 'Granite City' express?

4 What was the destination of the 'Cambrian Coast Express' from Paddington?

5 On which service did the 'Blue Pullmans' first appear on the Western Region in 1960?

6 Which titled train incorporated the only motor-driven Pullman cars in the world when introduced in 1932?

7 By the late 1970s, there was only one Pullman service on BR. What was its name?

8 Which named GWR train was the last broad gauge express to run from London to Cornwall on 20 May 1892?

9 Which named train ran between Waterloo and Ilfracombe from 1947 to 1954?

10 Which new name was adopted by the 'Capitals Limited' in 1953?

11 What was the traditional departure time of the 'Flying Scotsman' from King's Cross?

12 What name was assumed in 1947 by the LNER breakfast car express from Sheffield to Marylebone?

13 Across the Channel it was the 'Fleche d'Or', but in Britain it connected with which named express?

14 Which was the last of the ER 'Executives' to change from locomotive haulage to HSTs in 1981, having been the fastest locomotive-hauled train on BR?

15 Which named express carried a tartan headboard topped by a lion rampant?

16 What was the northern destination of the 'Pines Express'?

17 Which word was officially dropped from the title of the 'Cornish Riviera' in 1977?

18 Which was the first British streamlined train with a fully streamlined locomotive?

19 Which Brighton-Midlands express was worked in 1909 between Brighton and Rugby by a LB&SCR 4-4-2 tank engine throughout?

20 What was the new name of the 'Thames-Forth Express' adopted in 1957 and taken from part of the route over which it ran?

ON A PLATE

Unlike today's rather uninspiring, standardized nameplates, those of yesteryear were very distinctive. So much so that I have been able to make a puzzle out of them!

SO NAMED BY DRIVERS OF
THE NETHERLANDS STATE RAILWAYS
TO WHOM THIS LOCOMOTIVE WAS LOANED
1947-1952

What name *was* given to this locomotive, and what class was it?

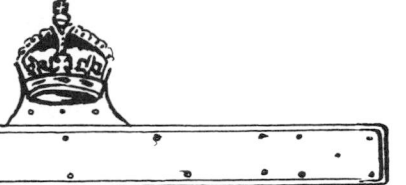

What name is missing from this LMS plate of 1937?

THE COTSWOLD

What symbol is missing from the top of this 1932 LNER plate?

H. L. I.

Another LMS plate, from 'Royal Scot' No 6121, and rather short on detail. However, from the shortest plate in the class, it became the longest when in 1949 it received its name in full. What was it?

And what is missing from this LNER plate, beneath the centre of the name?

IN MEMORY OF THE FALLEN
L.&N.W.R. EMPLOYEES
1914 – 1919

In memoriam. What name is missing from this 1937 plate, formerly *Croxteth*?

Which ex-LNER 'A4' 'Pacific' carried this metal plaque from 1954?

VALOUR
IN MEMORY OF
EMPLOYEES
WHO GAVE THEIR LIVES FOR THEIR COUNTRY
1914 – 1918

Which 1961 prototype diesel-electric locomotive carried this emblem, and who was the manufacturer?

And which company initials are missing from this 1920 plate?

WORKS TEAM

Below are the surnames of 31 former Locomotive Superintendents and Chief Mechanical Engineers, to be fitted into the grid according to their length. When all the names are in place, the two central rows will spell out the names of some of their workplaces.

4 Dean
Park
Reid
Urie
Webb

5 Adams
Ivatt
Marsh
Raven

6 Dunbar
Fowler
Holmes
Parker

7 Beattie
Bulleid
Gresley
Heywood
Kirtley
Pollitt
Stanier

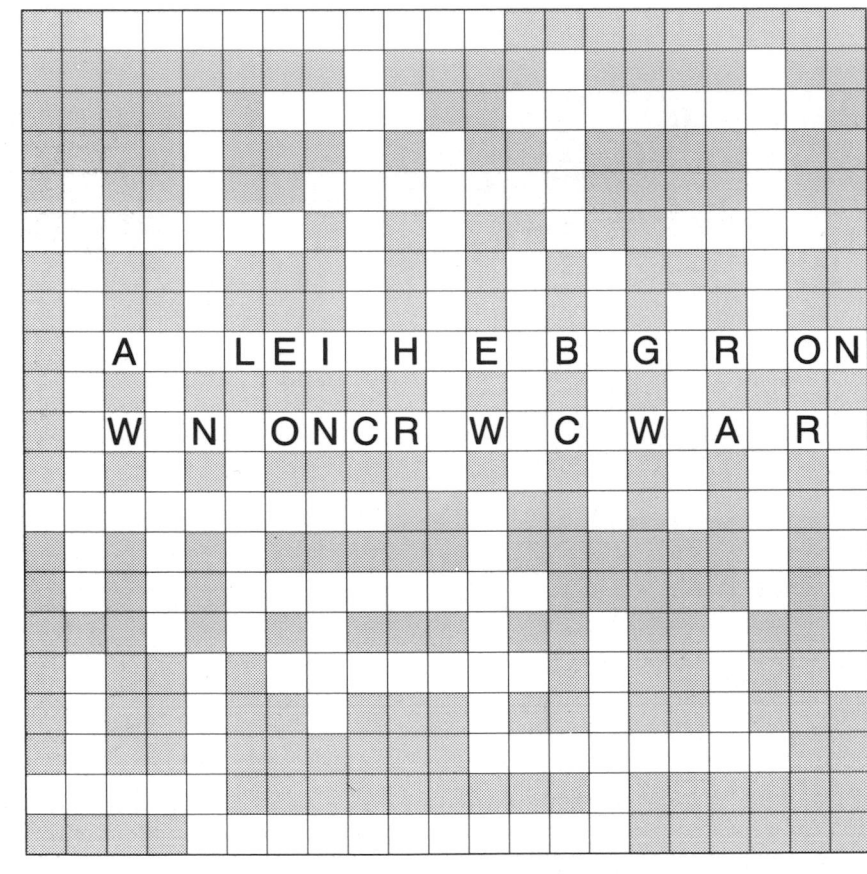

8 Archbutt
Aspinall
Drummond
Fairburn
Stirling

9 Billinton
Stroudley
Whitelegg

10 Churchward

11 Hurry-Riches
Pickersgill

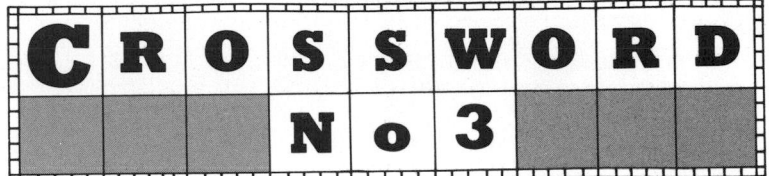

Across

4 Site of Britain's first water troughs, on the LNWR North Wales main line (4)

9 River Valley crossed by Harringworth viaduct, Northants, Britain's longest (7)

10 Kind of green used on Metropolitan and District locomotives (5)

11 Castle ——, junction for Yeovil and Weymouth (4)

12 Eastern, Western and Northern — but not Southern! (5)

13 Type of locomotive not in regular service on BR since 1968 (5)

14 An Edmondson is a type of this (6)

16 Colour of the locomotives of the Caledonian and Great Eastern railways (4)

17 —— *Glyndwr*, the Vale of Rheidol's No 7 (5)

18 'Road' giving its name to stations in Manchester and Nottingham (6)

25 First name of loco engineers Bury and Fletcher (6)

26 Cambridgeshire town saved by Driver Gimbert, who won the GC for driving his burning ammunition train away from it in 1944 (5)

27 —— Street, one of Uxbridge's GWR termini (4)

28 Name of Stephenson's follow-up to *Rocket*; also 'Jubilee' No 45545 (6)

30 American restaurant car! (5)

31 Name often given to the second of two distant or home signals operated by a single signal box (5)

32 15 down (LB&SCR), Kilbride (Caledonian) or Leake (GCR), maybe (4)

33 City served by Holbeck MPD (5)

34 Name of one of the locomotives participating in the Rainhill Trials (7)

35 Substance used to increase adhesion between driving wheel and rail (4)

Down

1 Northern terminus of the preserved Worth Valley line (8)

2 Preserved line based at Sheffield Park (8)

3 Railway branching west from Garstang on the West Coast Main Line to the sea near Fleetwood (5,3)

5 Colour of 44658 & Co! (5)

6 Hertfordshire town, at one time the furthest extension of the King's Cross-Cambridge electrification (7)

7 Driver's mate (7)

8 Euston, Victoria, Paddington, etc (7)

15 London & —— Railway, on which the first semaphore signals were installed in 1841 (7)

19 Material much used by Victorian railway engineers (4-4)

20 Kind of Passenger Train 49003 *City of Derby* was (8)

21 Material rapidly replacing 19 down in railway constructions! (8)

22 Ravenglass & —— Railway (7)

23 Goods yard locomotive (7)

24 What D232 was of Canada, and D233 of England (7)

29 'Jubilee' No 45672, named after an eighteenth-century admiral (5)

In this plan of an imaginary terminus station, the answers to the clues are entered in the boxes between signals reading from left to right (in the 'up' direction controlled by signals 1-16) or right to left (in the 'down' direction, signals 17-24A). In some cases, as in the case of the pointwork between 10/12 and 20/21, the lines are 'reversible', and words read in both directions. The last letter of each answer is the first of the next and falls in the shaded square adjacent to the signal controlling the next stretch of line. When the puzzle is completed, the squares at the buffer-stops, reading downwards, will spell out the name of a well-known terminus.

PLATFORM 1
UP RELIEF
PLATFORM 2
PLATFORM 3
UP MAIN
PLATFORM 4
DOWN MAIN
DOWN RELIEF
PLATFORM 5
PLATFORM 6
PLATFORM 7
PLATFORM 8

Up

1 (Up main distant) Type of ground signal (4)

2 (Up main-up relief home) Norfolk resort with both GER and M&GNJR termini (6)

3 (Up relief-platform 1) —— Lane, junction of the Metropolitan and Piccadilly lines near Ruislip, Middx (7)

4 (Platform 1 home) Worcester —— Hill (5)

5 (Up relief-platform 2) —— Park, LSWR junction south of Wimbledon (6)

6 (Platform 2 home) Colour of Britain's first streamlined train (6)

7 (Up relief-platform 3) Feature of a platform end (4)

8 (Platform 3 home) Terminus of the Cambrian Coast line (9)

9 (Up main home) King's —— (5)

10 (Up main-platform 4) West Coast Main Line summit (4)

11 (Platform 4 home) GWR junction at the English end of the Severn Tunnel (7)

12 (Up main-down main) Colloquially, motive power depot (4)

13 (Down main-platform 5) Railway's road lorry or cart, perhaps (4)

14 (Platform 5 home) Another GER and M&GNJR terminus in Norfolk (8)

15 (Down main-platform 6) Sand ——, device to arrest runaway vehicles beyond a trap point (4)

16 (Platform 6 home) Northern terminus of the North Yorks Moors Railway (8)

Down

17 (Down main advanced starter) Central, New or Wellington (5)

18 (Down main starter) Lamp checked by a signalman as the train passes (4)

19 (Down main intermediate home) American railway station (5)

20 (Platform 5 starter) Whitemoor or Wath, perhaps (4)

21 (Platform 6 starter) *Joyous* ——, Standard 4-6-0 No 73088 (4)

22 (Down relief starter) —— *Gow*, 'A3' No 60082 (4)

23 (Platform 7 starter) North Road or Bank Top (10)

23A (Platform 7 starter repeater) The real 'O' of the 'Old Worse and Worse'! (6)

24 (Platform 8 starter) Hayes & ——, GWR main line in Middx

24A (Platform 8 starter repeater) Welsh town nominally connected with Brecon by rail (5)

LONDON'S TERMINI

Turning now to real termini, here's a series of questions on London's main-line stations.

There's a lovely story told of St Pancras station regarding an American tourist walking in search of a local place of worship who mistakenly found himself in St Pancras station. He naturally reverently removed his hat in such hallowed surroundings and asked a smart railway employee — some sort of sidesman, he presumed — when the next service was. He was very taken aback to be given a list of train departures . . . !

1 Which terminus is approached by passengers through the Victory Arch, and what victory is being commemorated?

2 Which London terminus boasted the first railway hotel?

3 Which terminus at the time of its opening was the largest station in Britain?

4 From which terminus did the so-called 'Jazz Service' operate?

5 Which station provided the permanent terminus for the London & Greenwich Railway, London's first steam railway?

6 Until the Grouping, Victoria was two separate stations. One side was operated by the SE&CR. Who operated from the other?

7 Which object, much handled in freight by Midland trains from Burton, was used as the unit of measurement for the storage cellars beneath St Pancras?

8 What was the name of the North London Railway's City terminus?

9 Fenchurch Street was unique in that, after Grouping, it was owned by the LNER but used by which other company?

10 Which two London termini were described by Sir John Betjeman as the 'romance of Gothic and the romance of engineering . . . side by side'?

11 How many platforms does the GCR's terminus at Marylebone have?

12 From which London terminus does Hungerford Bridge provide the exit?

13 Euston was rebuilt in the 1960s, but only one other London terminus had been built in the twentieth century. Which one?

14 Which London terminus had surburban lines situated on the severely graded 'Hotel Curve'?

15 What was the Charing Cross after which the station was named?

16 Which terminal station's roof is famous for its iron and glass 'transepts'?

17 Which terminus boasts the Grosvenor Hotel?

18 In 1961, 75 architects and students with placards demonstrated outside Euston station, and a deputation met Prime Minister Harold Macmillan. What were they protesting about?

19 Beneath the words 'South Eastern & Chatham Railway' outside Victoria station was the name of another unexpected company which operated trains from the terminus. Which one?

20 Before Paddington was chosen, the GWR was intending to share its London terminus with another railway. Which one, at which station?

Picture question: Which London terminus is this, viewed from the Thames in 1977?

If you travel daily to and from work on the train — perhaps into one of the stations mentioned in the last quiz — here's a puzzle that should keep you busy for a couple of mornings; when all the answers are in place, the four long lines across will spell out a particularly suitable poetic quotation!

Grid lines (spelling out):
- O M T R - O E H S E N D S I L I F
- I G O N F O H S W F
- M A W O H V S N T K S T A N
- A N D H N R I E S B A C T S A V E A I

Across

12 Site of Whitemoor yard (5)
13 Familiar term for a signal (3)
14 The ——, 'A3' No 60060 (8)
16 Type of old carriage roof vent (7)
21 —— Elms (4)
23 William ——, No 60004 (8)
25 'Britannia' Burns (6)
28 The Midland had a Grand one at St Pancras (5)
35 Plant Works (9)
37 Junction for the Hayling Island branch (6)
41 Electric rail? (5)
42 Newark —— Trials, 1875 (5)

5 '—— Scotsman' (5)
6 GER Essex junction for Maldon and Bishops Stortford (6)
7 —— & Limpsfield (LB&SCR & SECR joint) (5)
8 2-6-2T (7)
9 Alternative name for a 125 (1,1,1)
10 —— —— Grenville, 'Lord Nelson' No 30853 (3,7)
11 'School' No 30900 (4)
13 Name applied to a power signal box (5)
15 'Jubilee' No 45735, or a Stephenson L&M loco (5)
17 Type of locomotive in Class '91' (8)
18 Ais —— (4)
19 GWR station between Gloucester and Ledbury (6)
20 '—— Mail' (5)
22 —— Oak Common (3)

24 Station at the foot of Camden bank (6)
26 Cornish resort, and No 34006 (4)
27 GWR, the 'Royal ——' (4)
29 —— Guardsman, No 46117 (5)
30 —— Town, MR London engine shed (7)
31 —— of Balmawhapple, 'D11/2' No 62691 (5)
32 Bon ——, 'A1' No 60154 (6)
33 British Protectorate, 'Jubilee' No 45633 (4)
34 The —— Howards, No 46133 or D9008
36 'The Long ——', Settle & Carlisle line (4)
38 Ill-fated 'tilting' train (1,1,1)
39 American sleeper (3)
40 —— Royal (3)
41 Number of cylinders on a 'Black Five' (3)

Down

1 —— of Australia, No 60012 (12)
2 73080 — Wizard . . . ! (6)
3 . . . and 73111 — King! (5)
4 Antelope, 'B1' No 61001 (5)

THE BIG FOUR I: LMS

The first of four puzzles dealing with each of the Groups during the years up to nationalization.

1 Whose statue used to stand in the old Great Hall at Euston?

2 What was the new and unusual title given to the post held by Josiah Stamp from 1926?

3 What was the original departure time of the 'Royal Scot' from Euston?

4 What was the original name by which the 2 pm 'Midday Scot' was known in LNWR days?

5 Who was the first Chief Mechanical Engineer of the LMS?

6 What name was used to describe Stanier's experimental locomotive No 6202?

7 What were the numbers of the two LMS diesel-electric locomotives of 1947, Britain's first designed for main-line use?

8 Which was the biggest marshalling yard on the LMS?

9 Why were water troughs installed *inside* Standedge Tunnel?

10 Which of these was *not* an LMS constituent company: Furness, Hull & Barnsley, North Staffordshire, London Tilbury & Southend?

11 What was the 'Ro-Railer', introduced by the LMS between Blisworth and Stratford-upon-Avon in 1942?

12 What were the two principal colours adopted for the LMS's 'Coronation Scot' train in 1937?

13 What was the record speed achieved by *Coronation* near Crewe on 29 June 1937?

14 In 1930, the LMS experimented with a modified 'Royal Scot' with a 900 psi high-pressure boiler. What was the locomotive's name?

15 What special type of engines were introduced by the LMS in 1927 to work the Toton-Brent coal trains?

16 Which city was the furthest south on the LMS system?

17 What was the number and name of Stanier's first 'Pacific' for the LMS?

18 In which American city was the World's Fair visited in 1939 by the LMS 'Coronation Scot' train?

BLESSED STATIONS!

Below is a list of towns and cities, and beside them a list of saints' names used as station names. See how quickly you can match up the town with its saint. (To make it more difficult, there's a 'red herring' town and saint — there are in fact only eight real pairs!)

Bedford _____ St Davids

Bristol _____ St Enoch

Cardiff _____ St James

Cheltenham _____ St Johns

Exeter _____ St Lukes

Exeter _____ St Marys

Glasgow _____ St Pancras

London _____ St Philips

Southport _____ St Thomas

PICTURE THE SCENE

ST PANCRAS

I guess there are no prizes for knowing that London was paired with St Pancras in the previous puzzle, so it's not too much of a giveaway to say that that is the venue for the next of the series of 'Picture the scene' puzzles. It's pre-125 days at the Midland terminus; 45135 *3rd Carabinier* waits to leave with an express for the Midlands in May 1976.

1 Between 1857 and 1868, when the Midland's extension to London was built, how did MR trains gain access to the capital?

2 What abolition effected by the Midland in 1875 revolutionized railway travel and forced other companies to improve passenger accommodation?

3 Which famous Victorian novelist was, as a young architect's assistant, involved in the building of the railway across St Pancras churchyard, in the distance on the left in this picture?

4 Approximately how many people were evicted without compensation to make way for the new terminus?

5 The signal box on the left of the picture was opened in 1957, but has now itself been replaced by a power box controlling the whole line almost to Wellingborough, Northants. Where is the new panel situated?

6 Just to the left of the 45's nose and in front of the nearer gas-holder can be seen the roof of an unusual Gothic Grade II listed building. What was its function?

7 Just behind the nose of the loco was the wagon hoist to the station's basement. What product was the basement designed to accommodate?

8 What was the original number of 45135?

9 Which department of BR occupied the former Midland Grand Hotel until recently?

10 What new non-railway complex is being built on the site of Somers Town goods station situated next door to St Pancras on Euston Road?

GETTING THE ROAD

Edinburgh Princes Street is mentioned in the 'Glasgow and Edinburgh' puzzle, and is only one of many stations using the name of a road as identification. Here are twelve more, but the towns and the thoroughfares have been separated. See how quickly you can pair them up again — but beware, for once again there is a 'red herring' in their midst. There are in fact only 11 true pairs!

Birmingham _____ Arkwright St

Bradford _____ Bridge St

Cheltenham _____ Foregate St

GLASGOW AND EDINBURGH

Moving now from London to Scotland's capital and principal city . . .

1   Which was Glasgow's first true passenger terminus?

2   Why were the spans of the original Glasgow Central railway bridge of unequal lengths?

3   The roof of Glasgow St Enoch shared its style and manufacturer with that of the London terminus of one of the English companies whose trains were to use it. Which terminus?

4   After the closure of St Enoch, Glasgow Central became in the early '70s Britain's busiest passenger terminus. How many trains were handled on an average weekday in November 1974 — 369, 693 or 963?

5   A plaque on Glasgow Central station was unveiled by the Queen on 7 May 1974. What did it commemorate?

6   What was the original means of propulsion on the 'Glasgow District Subway Railway' from 1897?

7   What familiar name was given to the electric trains running from Glasgow to Gourock etc?

8   How many platforms are there at Glasgow Central?

9   What is 'the Shell' on Glasgow Central?

10 Which Glasgow station was, perhaps surprisingly, described in 1842 as 'an almost fairy palace'?

11 For 66 years, something was missing from all trains entering Glasgow Queen Street. What was it?

12 Which station was the original western terminus of the Edinburgh & Glasgow Railway?

13 Which is the longest bridge on the original NBR Edinburgh to Glasgow line?

14 Which was the first proper station in Edinburgh?

15 When it was built, Edinburgh Waverley Station had more platform accommodation than any other British station except one. Which one?

16 Why is no part of Waverley Station more than 30 ft above rail level?

17 What was the original name of Waverley?

18 Edinburgh's North British Hotel adjoins Waverley Station; beside which station is Glasgow's 'NB'?

19 What was the name of the original terminus of the Caledonian Railway in Edinburgh before Princes Street was opened?

20 In 1971, six-coach dmus were replaced by six-coach trains of locomotive-hauled stock — but what was unusual about the formations?

Derby _____	Lime St
Exeter _____	Forster Sq
Leeds _____	Friargate
Liverpool _____	London Rd
Manchester _____	Malvern Rd
Northampton _____	Midland Rd
Nottingham _____	New St
Plymouth _____	Queen St
Worcester _____	North Rd

SCOTTISH THROATS

No — nothing to do with drinking inferior whisky . . . These throats are the railway kind, pictured in these photographs taken in the early 1970s. Can you identify them?

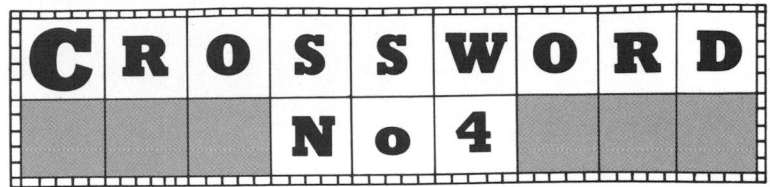

CROSSWORD No 4

Across

3 Name given to BR's first new Class '91' electrics (7)

7 Severn & —— Joint Railway (3)

9 'Deltic' No 7 (5)

10 Location of the GNR's Plant Works (9)

11 Plant which formed the headboard of the 'Flying Scotsman' in 'Deltic' days (7)

12 Bird of prey providing the name for 'A1' 'Pacific' No 60131 (6)

15 Station of the SER once known as Reigate Junction (7)

18 Dressed stone used as capping stones etc by railway architects (6)

21 System providing audible signal indications in a locomotive cab (1,1,1)

22 Bucks Golf Club with its own Platform on the GW&GC Joint line (6)

23 Drawn behind all locomotives except the 5 down variety (7)

25 Bird giving its name to a junction on the M&GNJR at Spalding (6)

31 City once containing General, Riverside and Queen Street stations (7)

32 North Wales Junction for a place of the same name (9)

33 Terminus of a GER branch in Essex, now part of the London 'Underground' (5)

34 Agreeable 'West Country' *Tor*, No 34026 (3)

35 Northants village paired with Glendon on the Midland main line (7)

Down

1 Railway number-taker! (7)

2 Former British territory remembered by 'Jubilee' No 45574 (5)

3 LSWR locomotive works and junction formerly known as Bishopstoke (9)

4 —— *Dempster Lines* (5)

5 Pannier, Saddle or Well? (4)

6 CME of the LSWR, 1878-1895 (5)

7 One of the vital substances carried by 23 across! (5)

8 No one complains when trains arrive thus! (5)

13 East African Railways (1,1,1)

14 Main lines are often thus named where there are multiple tracks (4)

16 River bridged — disastrously as it turned out — by Robert Stephenson in 1846 (3)

17 Part of a semaphore signal's equipment which might bear the name 'Adlake' (4)

19 GCR's well-preserved old 'Butler'! (9)

20 Beeching wielded an infamous one! (3)

22 Type of train built perhaps by Cravens, Metropolitan-Cammel or Birmingham RC&W (1,1,1)

24 L&YR station just west of Manchester Victoria (7)

25 Nickname for the Caledonian Railway (5)

26 Group of locomotives of the same type (5)

27 One might be granted for the establishment of a Light Railway (5)

28 Architect of the Midland Grand Hotel at St Pancras (5)

29 They supplied the names for Nos 6000-29 (5)

30 Architect of the Hotel Great Central, later BRB headquarters, 222, Marylebone Road (4)

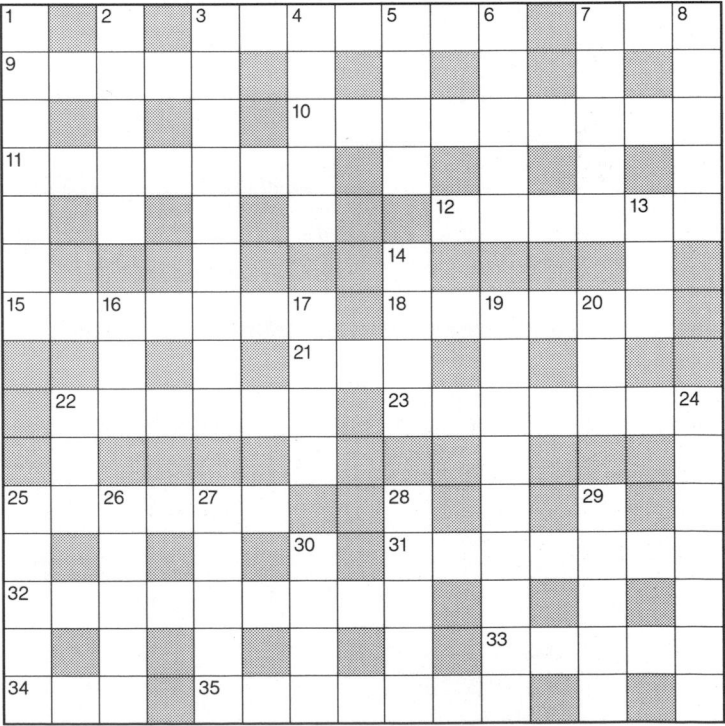

ROUNDHOUSE '62

Solve the 27 clues below and enter the answers in the spiral of this 'roundhouse', beginning at No 1 and moving in a clockwise direction. The last letter of each answer is the first of the next. When all the answers are in place, the five 'tracks' radiating from the centre (marked by the heavy lines) will contain the names of five engine sheds which were built on the roundhouse principle. Shed codes and associated information are based on the situation in 1962.

Clues

1 Preserved line with engines based at a shed at Wansford (4,6)

2 —— Town, shed 72C on the Southern (6)

3 15C 'Midland', or 15E 'Central' on the LMR (9)

4 Island shed 70H on the Southern (4)

5, 9 and 10 8A, principal LMR shed in the north-west, and the city in which it was situated (4,4;9)

6 65A, one of Glasgow's principal sheds (9)

7 Southampton ——, 71I (5)

8 8F, LMR shed at Wigan (7,6)

9 and 10 See 5

11 56F, shed on the former L&YR between Bradford and Dewsbury (3,4)

12 Bristol Bath —— (4)

13 Subshed of Gorton, near Glossop — now a preservation centre (7)

14 Lancaster (—— Ayre), or Bath (—— Park) (5)

15 —— Elms (4)

16 83C, ex-GWR West of England shed (6)

17 2A, principal LMR shed (5)

18 65G, former NBR shed north-west of Glasgow (5)

19 —— South, subshed of Guildford on the southern, or 81D on the Western (7)

20 52A, principal shed (and works) of the then North Eastern Region (9)

21 Tyne —— (4)

22 14B, Midland line shed outside St Pancras (7,4)

23 5A, Crewe —— (5)

24 55A, Leeds —— (7)

25 London terminus served by Top Shed (5,5)

26 87D, —— East Dock (not Cardiff!) (7)

27 Hull —— ——, subshed of Dairycoates (9,4)

From roundhouses to diesel depots, and stabled at this shed are eleven diesels. They're quite a collection — 'Deltics', Class '47s', even a High Speed Train. Solve the clues and enter the answers in the grid to read from left to right — the last letter of each answer is the first letter of the next. When completed, the two shaded columns will spell out the names of two important traction depots.

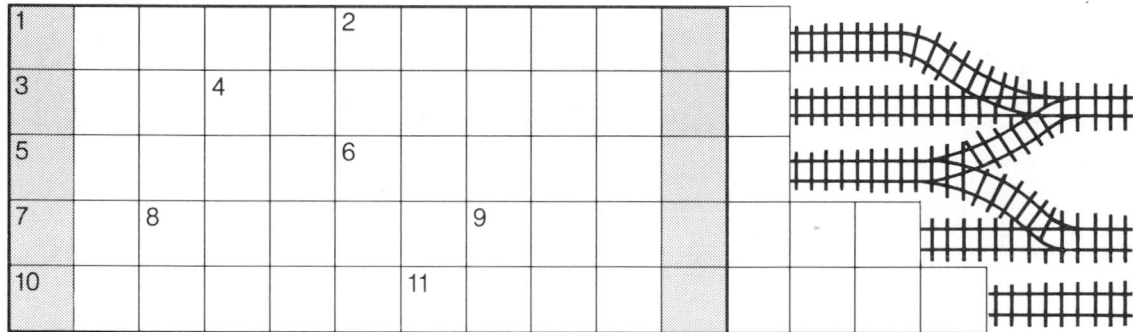

Clues

1 D10 of 1960 (6)

2 County after which 47170 was named in 1979 (7)

3 Norse god providing D1666's name in 1965 . . . (4)

4 . . . and an old-established GWR name given to D1661 in the same year (5,4)

5 47511's river of 1979 (6)

6 Ocean liner after which D230 was named in 1961 (6)

7 *Queen's —— Highlander* (D9004) (3)

8 D9020 of 1962 (6)

9 'Warship' D844 of 1961 (7)

10 —— Hill, Leeds depot giving its name to HST 43049 (7)

11 *Yeoman ——*, first named of Foster Yeoman's Class '59s' (9)

PACIFIC PUZZLE

The 'wheels' of this 'Pacific' 4-6-2 contain words relating to some of Britain's 'Pacific' steam locomotives. Each answer should be entered in an anti-clockwise direction.

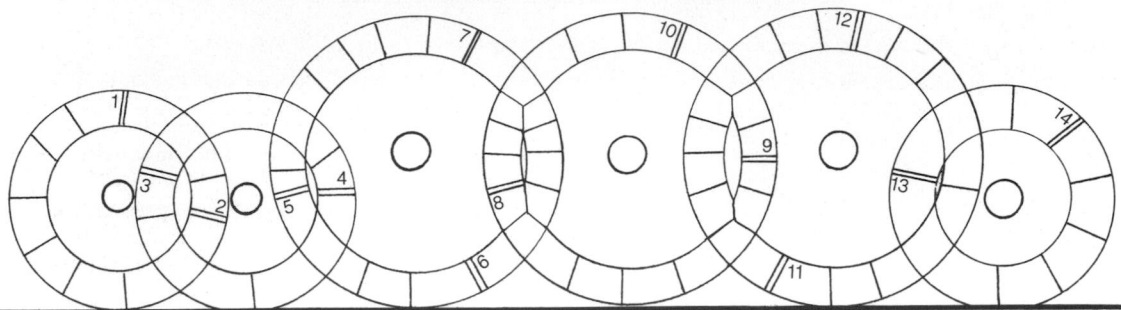

Clues

1 *Sir Eustace* ——, Southern Railway General Manager remembered on No 34090 (9)

2 —— *Line*, preserved 'Merchant Navy' 'Pacific' (4)

3 'A4' 'Pacific' designer, honoured by No 60007 (7)

4 God (or locomotive works?) commemorated by 'Britannia' No 70024 (6)

5 See 9

6 Wellington commemorated by 'Britannia' No 70014 (4,4)

7 William's surname borne by 'A4' No 60004 (8)

8 Britain's first 'Pacific', GWR's No 111, *The* —— —— (5,4)

9 and 5 Peppercorn 'A2' No 60532, named long before the days of children's TV! (4,4)

10 Novelist honoured by No 70033 (7)

11 Stanier's first streamlined 'Pacific' of 1937, No 6220 (10)

12 Duke who was the sole representative of BR's Class '8' 'Pacifics' (10)

13 —— *Firth*, the last 'Britannia' (7)

14 Word linked with Birmingham, Lancaster, Salford etc on Stanier 'Pacifics' (4)

Can you find the railway connections between these groups?

1 Hatton, Brent and Kings

2 The Iron Duke, *City of Truro*'s speed record and a Leeds terminus

3 GWR 4-6-0s No 1004 and No 1013, and the 'Pines Express'

4 Barnum, Concertina and Balloon

5 Shotlock Hill, Birkett and Moorcock

6 Brighton, Bournemouth and Devon

7 Stanier Class '5s', 'Deltic' 13 and 'Britannia' 8

8 Priory, Town and Harbour

9 A Railway Carriage & Wagon Company, Eastgate and No 71000

10 Glasgow, Cardiff and Exeter

11 Glasgow, Manchester and Leicester

12 Glasgow &, London & and Midland & (Joint)

CAB CONUNDRUM

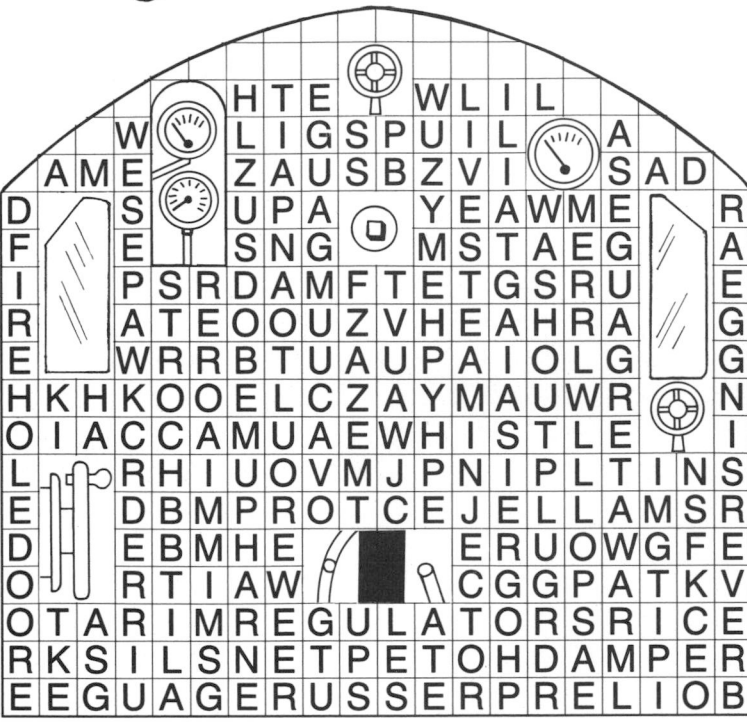

Finally, in this section dealing loosely with locomotive matters, hidden in this grid of letters forming a steam locomotive's cab are the names of 15 fittings and controls which might be found on the footplate. The words may read backwards, forwards or diagonally, up or down, but always in a straight line and never skipping letters. How quickly can you find them all?

13 London, Staffordshire and Eastern

14 *Novelty*, *Sans Pareil* and *Perseverance*

15 Valley, Beach and Tunnel

16 Defiance, Legacy and Troy

Picture link: Picture taken at the Midland Railway Centre at Butterley (inset) and the main picture

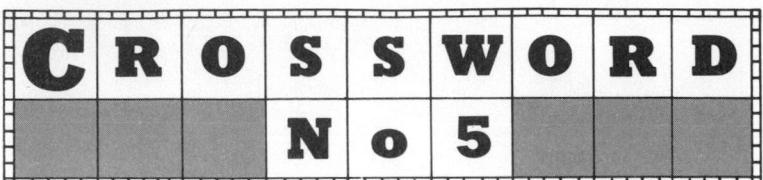

Across

1 and 6 The GNR's Locomotive Engineer, 1866-95 (7,8)

8 Nickname given to the concourse area of Paddington Station . . . (4)

10 . . . and the colloquial name of the first 'Underground' line to reach Paddington (3)

11 and 12 Waterloo's principal steam shed (4,4)

13 *Sir Frank* ——, 'Royal Scot' No 45530 (3)

15 Railwayman's term for a line or track (4)

17 Terminus of an NER branch from Melmerby on the Harrogate-Northallerton line (6)

20 Initials of the body that administered British Railways during and following nationalization (1,1,1)

22 Chief Mechanical Engineer of the LNWR, 1903-8 (5)

23 Number borne by 1 and 6 Across's most famous 'single' (3)

24 Station at the north end of the Caledonian's Solway Viaduct (5)

25 The NER's Locomotive Superintendent Mr Fletcher, to his friends? (3)

27 Colour of LNER 'Pacific' *Fox* (6)

29 Subdivision of a railway region (4)

30 Period of British rule in India remembered by several LMS 'Jubilee' locomotives! (3)

32 Wellington was such a Duke . . . (4)

33 . . . while a lesser nobleman provided the names for Nos 5043-62 . . . (4)

35 . . . built by this company (1,1,1)

36 Direction common to Grinstead, Garston and Didsbury (4)

38 Merseyside town served by both GCR and LNWR stations (2,6)

39 Early railway contractor who built 1,700 miles of British railways and once employed 45,000 men (7)

Down

1 Abbreviation for Pullman in the classification of Southern Region electric units (3)

2 Suffix used to distinguish stations at Hucknall, Stamford and Staveley (4)

3 Home of the 'King Arthur' Class, according to BR Standard No 73082? (7)

4 Member which forms the joint of the piston rod and connecting rod of a steam locomotive (9)

5 One of Ryde's three stations stood at the Head of one (4)

6 '—— chest', name given to the housing for the valves on a locomotive (5)

7 Viaduct — the longest concrete railway bridge in Scotland — on the West Highland Extension Railway (10)

9 River crossed by the well-known picturesque viaduct at Knaresborough on the NER (4)

14 Establishment which built 7,331 steam locomotives between 1843 and 1958 (5,5)

16 Locomotive Superintendant of the L&SWR, 1878-95 (5)

18 British Protectorate commemorated by 'Jubilee' No 45633 (4)

CALL TO ARMS

Something is missing from each of these railway coats of arms. Can you say what the missing people or objects are?

Great Central Railway

London & North Western Railway

London, Midland & Scottish Railway

Festiniog Railway

---

19 One of 30 on the GWR, from Torquay to Ramsbury (5)

20 Inaptly named signal box between Gas Works and Copenhagen Tunnels, King's Cross (5,4)

21 In which form telegraphic messages are sent between signal boxes (4)

26 'Western' D1036 (7)

28 These were affixed to the LNWR's slow line signal arms to distinguish them from main line indications (5)

29 River crossed by the 22 arches of Kirkstall Road viaduct, Leeds (4)

31 The only GWR 'King' whose monarch's name is not followed by a number (4)

34 The distances by which valves extend beyond the edges of steam ports in steam locomotives (4)

37 Bridge which fell disastrously on 28 December 1879 (3)

MONARCHS OF THE ROAD

Here are twenty questions with distinctly royal connections.

1 Which London terminus is named after a colossal statue of George IV, dismantled in 1845?

2 Queen Victoria made her first railway journey in 1842 — between which two places . . .?

3 . . . and which distinguished personage rode with Gooch on the footplate?

4 Which major station is approached across King Edward Bridge?

5 Which king's name appeared more often than any other on GWR 'King' Class locomotives . . .?

6 . . . and which was the most recent king featured?

7 Only one queen was commemorated by the 'Britannia' Class — who was she?

Picture question: Who designed this 'Royal' bridge?

8 For which company was Edinburgh's Princes Street station the terminus?

9 Name two cities which have or have had Queen Street stations.

10 Which company was dubbed 'the Royal Road'?

11 Which monarch's twenty-five year reign was commemorated by the LNER's 'Silver Jubilee' streamlined express . . .?

12 . . . and which monarch was commemorated by the train which was previously known as the 'Capitals Limited'?

13 Which member of the Royal Family was totally wrecked in the Harrow & Wealdstone crash of 1952?

14 Which river is crossed by the Royal Albert Bridge?

15 For which royal residence was Wolferton the local station?

16 What was the royal name of the LNER Pullman express from London to Scotland via Leeds and Harrogate introduced in 1928?

17 In which year did the 'Royal Scot' first run?

18 Which city was served by Kingmoor locomotive shed?

19 On the approaches to which London terminus is Royal Oak station?

PICTURE THE SCENE

WINDSOR AND ETON

While we're on the subject of royalty . . . The grandeur of the GWR's station at Windsor reflects the frequent use made of it by Queen Victoria and subsequent monarchs to and from the castle.

1 What was the name and the building company of Windsor's other station?

2 Which institution was heartily opposed to the building of the GWR main line and branch as they would undermine morals and discipline?

3 What fourth word was borne by the GWR's Windsor and Eton station to distinguish it from its rival?

4 What national event of 1897 prompted the rebuilding of the original Brunel train-shed of 1850?

5 Which station was used by royal travellers before the Windsor branch was built?

6 The GWR coat of arms seen above the screen contains the arms of two cities. Which are they?

7 Who was the last monarch to use the royal waiting room at the station?

8 Which company re-opened the waiting room with a 'Royalty and Railways' exhibition and replica royal train in 1983?

9 What is the name of the replica Dean 'single' standing at the platform?

10 Beyond the station, the branch crosses the oldest surviving Brunel iron bridge. What does it span?

THE PRESERVATION SCENE 1

The Dean 'single' at Windsor is a splendid engine, although it is only a non-working replica. However, there are plenty of real working locomotives to be seen up and down the country on our many preserved lines and steam centres. Here are a few questions concerning them.

1   Which was the world's first railway preservation scheme, formed in 1950?

2   Who, ironically, opened the preserved Dart Valley Railway in 1969?

3   Which well-known preservation society began life in 1961 as the 48XX Class Preservation Society?

4   Which line was the first standard gauge railway to re-open in preservation (1960) after closure by BR in 1958?

5   Which preserved line features Greenway Tunnel and Maypool Viaduct?

6   Which preserved railway was the brainchild of wildlife and railway artist David Shepherd?

7   A noted product of the Itchen Valley has given its name to a preserved railway — which one?

8   Where is 'Britannia' *Oliver Cromwell*'s home?

9   Which preserved line adopted the Berne loading gauge in order to be able to run continental stock?

10   What is the name of the bridge which carries the Severn Valley Railway over the Severn near Arley?

11   Which main line did the Main Line Steam Trust set out to rescue?

12   Which former engine shed forms the Standard Gauge Steam Trust's premises?

13   What was the material that the Leighton Buzzard Narrow Gauge Railway was built to carry in 1919?

14   What caused the building of a deviation line on the Festiniog Railway between 1965 and 1978?

15   What is the gauge of the Vale of Rheidol Railway?

16   From what does Wales' Gwili Railway derive its name?

17   Which is the lake in the name of the Lakeside & Haverthwaite Railway?

18   On which line did the restored Midland Railway signal box now used at Steamtown, Carnforth, formerly stand?

19   Which former MPD is now occupied by Steamport?

20   What is the wheel arrangement of the Beyer Peacock locomotives running on the Isle of Man Railway?

Picture question: 'U' Class 2-6-0 No 1618, seen here on the Bluebell Railway, was only the second locomotive to be rescued from Barry. She proved too heavy for her original home in preservation — where was it?

STEAM LINES

Can you tell on which preserved railway I took each of these four photographs?

Across

1 Acronym for BR's traffic control computer (4)

4 Of which a GWR 'single' was *Lord*, and, more recently, 87024 (5)

7 Railway company that developed Southampton Docks (1,1,1,1)

9 and 10 The 'Railway King' (6,6)

12 Vital ingredient of an Acme Thunderer! (3)

13 Portsmouth suburban station on the 7 across and LB&SCR Joint (7)

15 Dorset village served by the picturesquely named Wishing Well Halt (5)

18 Initially, a train of passenger vehicles not carrying passengers (1,1,1)

19 GER Cambridgeshire station from which 6 lines radiated (3)

20 Department of the War Office dealing with rail transport overseas (1,1,1)

21 Terminal platform(s) contained within a larger platform (3)

22 'A1' 'Pacific' No 60084 (5)

23 That of a semaphore signal at 'off' is between 45° and 60° (5)

25 Material for which a 'pan' was provided on steam locomotives (3)

26 and 20 down Flagship locomotives D601 and 50035 (3,5)

27 Initially speaking, the abortive No 49003 *City of Derby* (1,1,1)

28 Amount that a steam valve extends beyond the admission ports when in mid-position (3)

29 MR Hope Valley station between Hope and Chinley (5)

30 NER's first resident architect, and the designer of York station etc (7)

34 Predecessor of the GC before 1897 (1,1,1)

35 *Oor* ——, very Scottish 1985 name of Class '37' 37402 (6)

37 King whose bridge is crossed on the approaches to Newcastle Central (6)

38 That of Lochalsh was reached by railway in 1897 (4)

39 Devices that support the walls of the firebox within the boiler casing (5)

40 GWR class designed by Collett and introduced in 1927 (4)

Down

2 Eastern terminus of the Central Line (5)

3 —— Green, signal box on the climb to Shap (5)

5 Stroudley 'Terrier' No 55, preserved on the Bluebell Railway (7)

6 Smoke and spent steam escaping from a locomotive chimney (7)

7 The biggest of the 'Big Four' (1,1,1)

8 *Hal o' the* ——, No 60116 and, more recently, 87031 (4)

11 Much-photographed sea-wall station on the GWR's South Devon line (7)

14 East end of the Metropolitan Railway 'Widened Lines' (7)

16 Company owning and operating Class '59s' from Merehead Quarry (7)

17 Familiar name of the Class '35' Beyer Peacock diesel-hydraulics (5)

20 See 26 across

21 Locomotive manufacturer based in Stafford (7)

24 One of many in a steam locomotive's superheater (7)

25 One of the principal stations on the Settle & Carlisle line (7)

31 Code-name for a ballast train brake van (5)

32 Kind of junction where different companies' lines joined without pointwork! (3-2)

33 'Right ——!' — guard's cry (4)

36 LSWR terminal station, 'on Solent' (3)

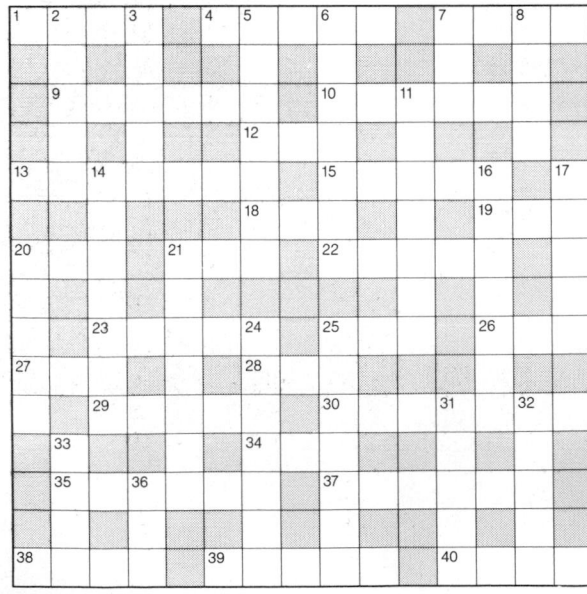

MARSHALLING

See how quickly you can marshal these 10 'wagons' to form a single 'train' in such a way that the words on adjoining 'wagons' form two-word expressions with railway connections. The odd words at the front and end of the 'train' will, of course, be 'red herrings' and have no partners. Thus, HIGH/GREAT, BELLE/CHIME, WHISTLE/HORN, WESTERN/SOUTHERN would be marshalled as HIGH/GREAT WESTERN/SOUTHERN BELLE/CHIME WHISTLE/HORN and so on.

1		2		3	
MAIL	BLACK	HOUSE	SHED	ENGINE	DRIVING

4		5		6		7	
BRASS	IRON	LAMP	LIGHT	WHEELS	ROUND	SCOT	IRISH

8		9		10	
FOOT	HAND	DUKE	ROYAL	FIVE	FOUR

INITIAL REACTION

What do each of the following railway initials stand for?

1 LTSR

2 SMJR

3 BTC

4 MS&LR

5 WLER

6 BRUTE

7 C&W

8 ECS

9 MAS

10 CWR

WHERE'S THE STATION?

How quickly can you spot the railway place-name hidden in each of these sentences?

1 Three miles south of here a train would enter Blea Moor Tunnel.

2 Lines from here reach Selby or Knaresborough.

3 Southern bank — locomotives had to make a rush on it on down trains!

4 Over all others, this GWR town's products win — don't they?

5 Where there is preserved a splendid coterie of GWR engines.

6 Railway centre rather trodden asunder by Crewe after the Grouping.

7 Whence expresses might take us to North Western destinations.

8 Where BR do very good cross-Channel business

9 Before Shap, rest on the line between here and Lancaster.

10 Hold-ups here left the Midland very much itching for its own route to London!

HERE AND THERE

Many stations, situated inconveniently far from two villages, took the names of both to disguise the fact and perhaps to widen their 'catchment area'. Here are ten jumbled examples — can you match up the correct pairings? (The company initials after the second name indicate the railway ownership of that name and its correct partner.)

Goring & Street (S&DJR)

Craven Arms & Garsdale (MR)

Glendon & Latimer (Met & GCR)

Hawes Junction & Bulwell (GNR)

Hayes & Stokesay (LNWR)

Basford & Streatley (GWR)

Knowle & Birstall (GCR)

Glastonbury & Rushton (MR)

Chalfont & Dorridge (GWR)

Belgrave & Harlington (GWR)

THREE INTO ONE

First identify the locations of the junctions sketched below, then write the name of each in the boxes. Next transfer the letters to the correspondingly numbered boxes in the lower row to spell out the name of an interesting old railway.

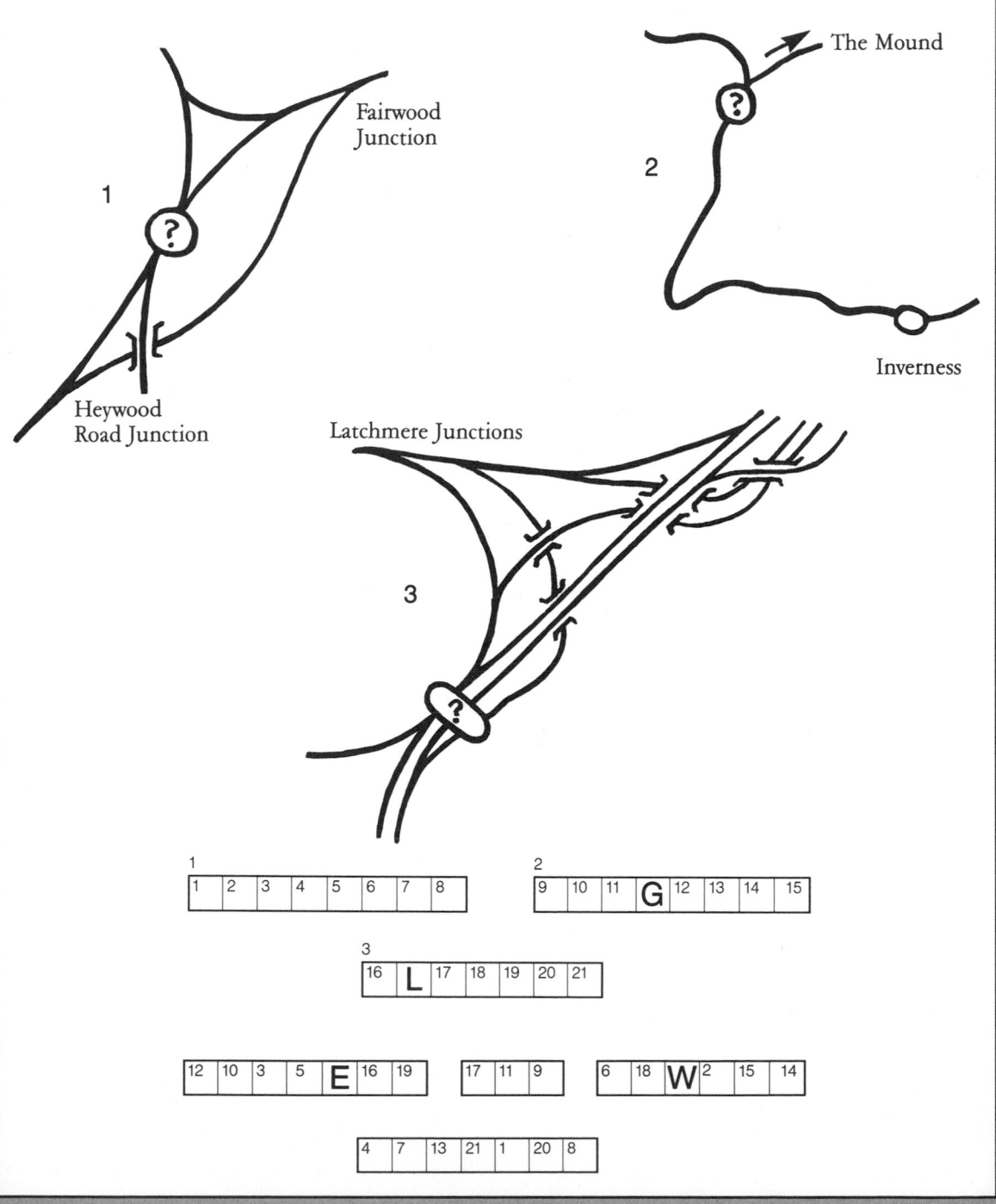

Fairwood Junction

1

Heywood Road Junction

The Mound

2

Inverness

Latchmere Junctions

3

1							
1	2	3	4	5	6	7	8

2							
9	10	11	G	12	13	14	15

3						
16	L	17	18	19	20	21

12	10	3	5	E	16	19

17	11	9

6	18	W	2	15	14

4	7	13	21	1	20	8

EMPTY STOCKI

Find the answers to this crossword by filling the 'empty' blanks in the clues, which are all railway names, places or phrases. A few company initials have been given as additional hints.

Across

1 Boston —— Works (5)
4 —— North Western (5)
7 *Saint* —— (60145) (5)
8 —— Main Line (GWR) (5)
10 —— Mechanical Engineer (5)
13 —— Summit (HR) (4)
14 Stewarts —— (4)
15 —— Midland, or —— Central (5)
22 Sir Josiah —— (5)
23 —— -coupled (5)
24 —— *Dempster Lines* (5)
25 —— and Claremont (LSWR) (5)

Down

1 Liverpool —— Street (4)
2 See picture clue
3 Glasgow St —— (5)
4 George —— (LNWR) (5)
5 4 across Wall —— (4)
6 —— Valley Railway (4)
9 —— Works Tunnel (GNR) (3)
10 Restaurant —— (3)
11 —— shunting (3)
12 Audley —— (3)
16 —— Holloway, or —— Sydenham (5)
17 'Southern ——' (5)
18 17 down —— signal box (King's Cross) (4)
19 —— drag (4)
20 ——gorm Works (HR) (4)
21 *The Great* —— (4)

Picture clue: —— Head Viaduct (4)

SLIP COACHES I

Answer the clues and enter the answers in the appropriate column of the upper grid, reading downwards. Then 'slip' the three letters in the shaded squares down into the lower grid; when all the slipped letters are in place, the lower grid will spell out a quotation from *Meet Mr Mulliner*, by P. G. Wodehouse. The bold lines indicate breaks between words.

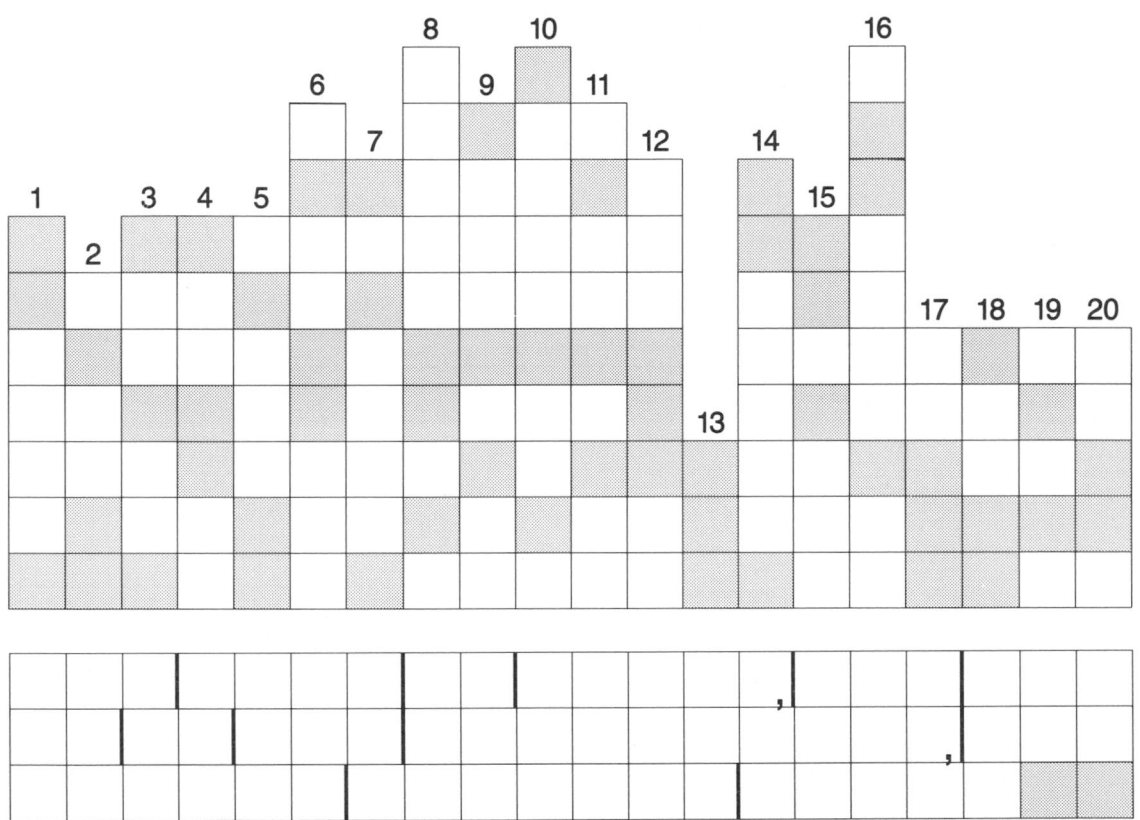

Clues

1 GWR main line junction for the Henley on Thames branch, which had a daily slip coach from 1874 to 1914 (7)

2 E. L. ——, 19th century railway writer and expert (6)

3 LSWR terminus reached from Exeter or Sidmouth Junction (7)

4 —— & Northern Counties Railway, 'foreign' line absorbed by the Midland in 1903 (7)

5 'A3' 'Pacific' No 60088 (4,3)

6 LMS named train introduced in 1927 (5,4)

7 Preserved LMS 'Jubilee' Class No 5593 (8)

8 GWR named train introduced in 1935 (10)

9 Welsh narrow gauge railway incorporated in 1836 (9)

10 Lynton & —— Railway (10)

11 GWR junction just south of Hereford on the Gloucester line (9)

12 Brand-name of the car-carrying train service introduced by BR in 1956 (8)

13 *Sir* ——, 'King Arthur' No 30450 (3)

14 Locomotive Engineer of the GNR, 1866-95 (8)

15 Descriptive of Robert Stephenson's original Menai Bridge (7)

16 —— & Montgomeryshire Railway (10)

17 River crossed by the Royal Border Bridge (5)

18 —— *Martin*, 'West Country' No 34043 (5)

19 'City' credited with 102¼ mph on Wellington Bank in 1904 (5)

20 —— Street, North London Railway terminus (5)

RAILWAYS IN FILM AND FICTION

Many preserved lines earn a good slice of their income from the activities of film and TV companies, and railways have always been popular subjects or backdrops to well-known works of fiction. How well-read or observant are you . . .?

1   What was the name of the railway company in E. Nesbit's children's classic *The Railway Children*?

2   Which preserved line was used when the book was filmed in 1972?

3   Which LMS station, now home of a preservation centre, featured prominently as the setting for Trevor Howard and Celia Johnson's *Brief Encounter* in 1946?

4   Which East Midlands preserved line was 'transported' to East Germany for the Bond film *Octopussy*?

5   In which Victorian play was the hero discovered in 'the cloakroom at Victoria station . . . The Brighton Line'?

6   On which railway bridge did Richard Hannay (Robert Donat) climb out of a moving train to evade his pursuers in the 1938 film *The Thirty-nine Steps*?

7   Which real-life veteran locomotive took the title role in the 1953 Ealing classic *The Titfield Thunderbolt*?

8   In which famous Victorian story was the heroine berated by her fellow passengers: 'Don't keep him [the Guard] waiting, child! Why, his time is worth a thousand pounds a minute!'?

9   *Night Mail* was a celebrated early British film documentary produced by the GPO film unit with verse by W. H. Auden and music by Benjamin Britten. Which mail train route did it follow?

10   *Murder, She Said* was the 1962 film version of the Agatha Christie whodunit *4.50 From ——* — which London terminus?

11   Can you identify the place-name in this verse from a well-known poem?
'The steam hissed. Someone cleared his throat.
No one left and no one came
On the bare platform. What I saw
Was —— — only the name.'

12   Which fictional school took over the Longmoor Military Railway in 1966 to stage their own 'Great Train Robbery'?

13   *Robbery*, a film dramatisation of the Great Train Robbery, was filmed on the former Rugby-Market Harborough line in 1967, but when and where did the real event occur?

14   Charles Dickens wrote a series of stories under the title *Mugby Junction*. On which real-life junction was the place based?

15   Who was the station-master at Buggleskelly, supposedly in Ireland but actually in Hampshire?

16   Several of the leading characters in the Ealing black comedy *The Ladykillers* (1955) meet their end over the portals of a set of tunnels — which ones, and outside which London terminus?

17   In the British *Great Railway Journeys of the World* (BBC), Michael Palin travelled by rail from London to which Scottish terminus?

18   The Quainton Railway Centre was turned into 'India' for which major ITV drama series?

19   Which English poet wrote a poem to protest against the building of the Kendal & Windermere Railway in 1844? ('Is there no nook of English ground secure/From rash assault?')

20   Which GWR West Country branch was used in the film of *The Hound of the Baskervilles* in 1931?

FACTS AND FIGURES

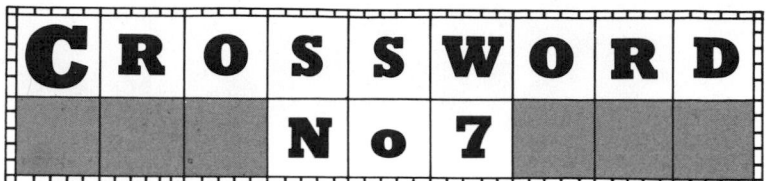

All the answers in this crossword are numbers, whether years, locomotive numbers, class numbers or whatever.

Across

1 Age of the L&MR's oldest surviving locomotive, *Lion*, in 1989 (3)

3 World record speed in mph attained by *Mallard* in 1938 (3)

5 The electrified West Coast Main Line operates at this number of Kv (2)

6 Number of '5700' Class 0-6-0 tanks built, the GWR's largest class (3)

7 Wheel formation of 38 across (1-1-1)

9 Number of years of independent existence of the GWR between incorporation and nationalization (3)

11 Wheel formation of Webb's very successful four-cylinder compound mineral engine for the LNWR (1-1-1)

13 Class number of a recent group of locomotives based at Toton, Notts, and primarily used on 'merry-go-round' trains (2)

14 *Duchess of Hamilton* (5)

17 Number of the first of the Isle of Wight's '02' Class of 0-4-4 tanks, *Fishbourne* (2)

18 Wheel formation of preserved Standard tank 80079 (1-1-1)

19 Number of production 'Deltics' (2)

20 Class number of former numbers D11-D137 (2)

21 BR number of 'A4' streamlined 'Pacific' *Commonwealth of Australia* (5)

22 700——, *Oliver Cromwell*, preserved 'Britannia' at Bressingham (2)

23 1 in ——, steepest part of Shap incline, northbound (2)

24 Wheel formation of Fowler's '7F' Class built specially for the S&DJR (1-1-1)

25 Age at which the GNR's Patrick Stirling died, still in office (2)

27 Number of WCML electric locomotive *King Arthur* (5)

30 Class number of the largest class of diesels on BR, the 350 hp shunters, formerly D3000-D4192 (3)

32 Number of Riddles 'Austerity' 2-10-0, now named *Gordon* (3)

34 Number of route miles owned by the Highland Railway (1 less than *Butler Henderson*!) (3)

35 Wheel formation of 14 and 20 down (1-1-1)

36 Number of miles (in round figures) between King's Cross and Edinburgh Waverley (3)

37 Number of wheels on the locomotive of 16 down (2)

38 Number of the NRM's *Hardwicke* (3)

39 Last three digits of the number of the last steam locomotive built by Crewe (and BR's highest numbered loco) (3)

Down

1 Year in which the Quintinshill collision, Britain's worst railway disaster, occurred (4)

2 Number of the NRM's *Cornwall* (3)

3 Year in which a full electric service began between Euston and Manchester (4)

4 Number of Stanier's 'Turbomotive' on the LMS (4)

5 Original 'D' number of preserved Class '40', 40122 (3)

8 BR number of SR 'N15' loco bearing the same name as 27 across (5)

10 Year in which the Stockton & Darlington Railway opened (4)

12 ——A, shed number of Old Oak Common (2)

14 Numerically, the first 'Black Five' (BR number) (5)

15 Gresley/Metro-Vickers Bo-Bo electric named *Tommy* in 1950 (5)

16 Number of the last steam locomotive constructed for British Railways (5)

20 BR number of the only 'Black Five' with Stephenson link motion valve gear, now preserved as *George Stephenson* (5)

22 Preserved Midland Compound 4-4-0 (or *Western Enterprise*, or *County of Middlesex*!) (4)

26 19——, the year 16 down was outshopped (2)

28 The Great Western's 'Castle' *Great Western* (4)

29 Time when the 'Cornish Riviera' left on its 'Limited' run to Penzance (2:2)

31 'D' number of the first 'Clayton' Class '17' Bo-Bo diesel-electric (4)

33 Wheel formation of the GWR '1400' Class tanks used for push-pull workings (1-1-1)

34 Number of 'A2' 'Pacific' *Blue Peter* as preserved (and which it never carried in service) (3)

THE BIG FOUR II: LNER

1 The LNER adopted the motto of one of its constituents for its coat of arms — which one?

2 In 1923, one-third of the LNER's total locomotive stock was of one type of wheel arrangement — 2,500 in all. Which type?

3 The first Chairman of the LNER was the grandfather of a well-known Conservative politician and peer of our own day. Who?

4 Which two letters were used to identify LNER goods stock?

5 Gresley's most massive locomotive was employed on the Worsborough incline. What type was it?

6 Which class of LNER steam locomotives included both *Sandringham* and *Arsenal*?

7 What was the number of Gresley's so-called 'Hush-Hush' high-pressure experiment of 1929?

8 What was unusual about the five-car coach sets introduced by Gresley for the London-Leeds service?

9 In 1930, a London-Leeds train set was fitted with radio facilities, each passenger being supplied with headphones. A record player was also fitted — why?

10 In 1935, a special coach on the same route attracted 35,000 patrons at 1s (5p) a head. What was it?

11 What special name was given to the 100th Gresley 'Pacific'?

12 What was the prototype 'V2' 2-6-2 No 4771 *Green Arrow* named after?

13 What kind of train was the LNER's 'Northern Belle', introduced in 1933?

14 Where was the LNER's New England freight yard?

15 The LNER boasted Britain's first mechanized marshalling yard, completed in 1929. Where was it?

16 In acreage terms, the three largest stations on the LNER were Edinburgh Waverley, Liverpool Street and — which?

17 Why did the 'Coronation' streamline train set have two kitchen cars but no dining car?

18 What were most of the 1922-5 batches of Gresley 'Pacifics' named after?

19 Gresley's senior headquarters assistant moved to become CME of one of the other 'Big Four' companies in 1937. Who was he?

20 Which was the only named train to run on the former Great Central section of the LNER?

DELTIC DILEMMA

Talking of the LNER, perhaps the most celebrated locomotives to run on the East Coast Main Line in more recent times were the 'Deltics'. Here are the names of eight of them, jumbled up to form seven new ones. Can you sort them out?

The Duke of Wellington's Paddy

_____

Gordon Grey

_____

The Green Pinza

_____

Howards Watch

_____

The Black Saint

_____

Royal Scots Nimbus

_____

Highlander Regiment

_____

ST NEOTS

'Deltic' days on the East Coast Main Line: 9017 *The Durham Light Infantry* heads a down express towards St Neots station in June 1973, the year that the prototype HST began trials . . .

1 In 1973, 9010 *The King's Own Scottish Borderer* became the first 'Deltic' to pass a certain landmark. What was it?

_____

2 During the year, the four-digit headcode carried by the 'Deltics' was replaced — by what?

_____

3 What other change in the identification of the locomotives took place at the end of the year?

_____

4 9017 was a North-east-based 'Deltic', which were named after local regiments. What were the London-based locomotives named after?

_____

5 Although most ended their days at York, all of the 'Deltics' had been previously allocated between three sheds. Which were they?

_____

6 The East Coast Main Line is quadruple track all the way from London to beyond St Neots except for one stretch. Where is this, and why?

_____

7 The signal facing the train at the end of the platform has a black arm pivoted within an illuminated glass-fronted circular white frame. By what name is this type of signal known, and what is its function?

_____

8 What colour was the enamel station nameboard seen on the down platform?

_____

9 The first of a certain type of lineside sign was erected on the ECML between Stoke Summit and Lolham in 1964, reflecting the arrival of the 'Deltics'. What sign was it?

_____

10 *The Durham Light Infantry* headed the last 'Deltic'-hauled service train out of King's Cross on the last day of which year?

_____

SPEED CURVE

126 mph

One of the most notable events ever to occur on the East Coast Main Line was *Mallard*'s record-breaking run of 1938, the fiftieth anniversary of which was celebrated with so much vigour last year — so here's a puzzle all about speed! Answer the clues and enter the answers into the grid, reading downwards. Their last letters, read across, will spell out a famous high-speed event of 1888, and again in 1895.

1. 'Colour' of the locomotive that attained 113 mph near Tallington on the ECML in August 1936 (6)

2. Class of GWR 4-4-0 locomotives of 1900 which were, according to O. S. Nock, the 'fastest . . . yet to run on British metals' (6)

3. Name of LNWR 2-4-0 No 1306 which ran non-stop from Euston to Carlisle in 1895 at an average of 51 mph (5)

4. Class of GWR engines, one of which made the fastest ever run on the 'Bristolian' at an average of 75.4 mph (6)

5. Western end of a run from Paddington made at a start-to-stop average of 67 mph — in 1846! (6)

6. —— *Abbey*, 'Star' No 4072, which made the fastest end-to-end run on the 'Cheltenham Flyer' prior to 1931 (6)

7. Designer of the NER 2-4-0 No 1475 which travelled between York and Newcastle in 1888 at an average speed of 62 mph (7)

8. 'Princess' which made a record average speed of 68.2 mph between Euston and Glasgow in November 1936 (9)

9. LNWR record-breaking 'Precedent' 2-4-0 No 790, now preserved in the National Collection (9)

10. Driver of *Mallard* for the record run of July 1938 (10)

11. Locomotive which broke the 100 mph barrier on Wellington Bank in 1904 (4,2,5)

12. McIntosh class of 4-4-0s of 1896, one of which attained a sustained maximum of 85½ mph which remained a record on the Caledonian until LMS days (11)

13. SR express which, in the 1930s, hauled by No 777 *Sir Lamiel*, attained a start-to-stop record of 69.2 mph between Salisbury and

Waterloo, believed to be an absolute record for the line (8,5)

14. Designer of the locomotive which made the run referred to in clue 5 (3,6,5)

125

Can you identify these InterCity 125 power car names from just their first, second and fifth letters?

TWENTY QUESTIONS

Each of these twenty questions is to do with a number — from one to twenty.

1 Who was the designer of the GNR's famous 'Single' No 1?

2 222 Marylebone Road was for many years BRB Headquarters — but what railway-operated building had it been previously?

3 Which tunnel, just over 3 miles long, lies between Marsden and Diggle?

4 Which was the biggest of the 'Big Four'?

5 How many 'Black Fives' were built — 482, 842 or 1,024?

6 What is the meaning of the emergency signalbox telegraph code of '6 bells'?

7 The Vale of Rheidol's No 7 and 'Britannia' No 70010 are both named after a Welsh patriot — which one?

8 On which English preserved line were the railway sequences for the Bond film *Octopussy* shot?

9 Which London terminus replaced Nine Elms when it was opened in 1848?

10 Which famous express was also known as the '10.30 Limited'?

11 Which, at over 11,000 ft, is Britain's longest railway bridge?

12 The only 12 miles of narrow gauge line operated by British Rail were sold recently — what is the line called?

13 'Britannia' No 70013 was the last still active in August 1968 and is now preserved — what is its name?

14 What was the name of George Stephenson's first locomotive of 1814, which sounds as though it should have been travelling to Waterloo?

15 The 'Long Drag' stretches for 15 miles at an almost constant 1 in 100 gradient — on which line?

16 Which railway body was set up by 16 railway companies in 1845?

17 In 1987, HST No 43017 was named after a TV station — which?

18 At the turn of the century, one London terminus with its 18 platforms handled more trains and passengers than any other — which?

19 Which transport body was established in August 1919?

20 Which East Anglian railway boasted a station called Twenty?

Across

1 Street giving its name to Edinburgh's 3 down terminus . . . (7)

5 . . . and the name of Glasgow's G&SWR terminus (2,5)

8 Controlling handle on a steam locomotive (9)

9 —— House, London docklands station on the GER's Woolwich/Beckton branch (6)

12 River crossed by the 19-arch viaduct of the same name near Chirk, Britain's longest when built (3)

13 One of the nicknames for a ground signal (5)

16 *Blink* ——, 'A3' No 60051 (5)

17 Name given to the railway amalgamations of 1923 (8)

20 *The Fife and Forfar* ——, 'Deltic' '6' (8)

21 'The —— Mail', LNWR express instituted in 1848 (5)

24 'Slow, —— and Jolty', nickname of the Stratford-on-Avon & Midland Junction Railway (5)

25 Number of through platforms at Cambridge station (3)

26 Type of institution providing the names for Maunsell's Southern Railway 'V' Class 4-4-0s (6)

29 What is driven by the diesel engine of a diesel-electric locomotive to supply the power (9)

30 Residue of fused ash blocking a fire-grate — the fireman's bane! (7)

31 Distinguishing name for a certain company's stations in Loughborough, Leicester and Rugby, for instance (7)

Down

2 'Peak' D7 (12)

3 Company responsible for the operation of the Callendar and 28 down Railway (10)

4 Famous junction of the MR Lancaster and Carlisle lines north of Hellifield (6)

5 Title of Gareth, Brian and Ontzlake, according to the 'King Arthurs' (3)

6 Loch at the south end of which was the North British's Fort Augustus branch (4)

7 The unequal bogie configuration of the Class '28' diesel-electrics gave this unusual wheel arrangement code (2-2)

8 Town with Pier Head, Esplanade and St Johns Road stations (4)

10 Gricer? (5-7)

11 *Saint* ——, 'A1' No 60145 (5)

14 Home of the National Railway Museum (4)

15 —— —— Railway, the world's first public railway (6,4)

18 Inventor of a 'lock and block' system of signalling (5)

19 Toby was such an engine in the Rev Awdry's stories! (4)

22 Word often applied to, for instance, the Midland's route through the Peak District (6)

23 A Great one supplied the name for Britain's first 'Pacific', No 111 of the GWR (4)

27 'Welsh steam', perhaps (4)

28 Highland Railway terminus opened in 1880 (4)

29 Railway of which Ivatt was Locomotive Superintendent from 1895 to 1911 (1,1,1)

THE NATIONAL COLLECTION

1 Which railway company opened the first museum in Britain devoted exclusively to railways?

2 The new National Railway Museum replaced four previous sites at York, Clapham, Glasgow and — where?

3 A special NRM train made up entirely of a certain type of vehicle formed the 'Centenary Special' round-Britain train in 1979. What were the vehicles and what was the centenary?

4 Which class of steam locomotive appears in 'sectioned' form in the NRM — and what was its original name?

5 What is unusual about the Port Carlisle 'Dandy' No 1, one of the museum's early carriages?

6 Which Duke's private saloon of 1899-1900 is featured in the Collection?

7 What kind of special carriage is the preserved WCJS vehicle No 186?

8 What kind of vehicle is 'Topaz'?

9 Queen Victoria travelled in the preserved Royal Saloon of 1869, but who used that of 1842?

10 What is the nickname of the Bury-type 0-4-0 No 3 of the Furness Railway?

11 What name is borne by the NRM's working reproduction of a Gooch broad gauge 'single'?

12 The GNR's *Henry Oakley* was the first of a type of steam locomotive to run in Britain. Which type?

13 Where is the NRM's *Caerphilly Castle* to be found?

14 Which company has indefinitely loaned *Duchess of Hamilton* to the NRM?

15 Preserved 1500V DC electric locomotive No 26020 took the first official train through which new tunnel in 1954?

16 Built in Britain in 1935, 4-8-4 No 607 has now returned to join the National Collection — from where?

17 Which branch of railway operation is represented by the museum's 'stirrup frame'?

18 On which preserved line did Stirling 'single' No 1 return to steam after 42 years in 1981?

19 Which events of 1895 involving LNWR No 790 *Hardwicke* led to her preservation?

20 The National Collection includes two 'Deltics'. One is the *King's Own Yorkshire Light Infantry* — what is the other?

ROCKET 150

In 1980, the 150th anniversary of the Liverpool & Manchester Railway was marked with three days of celebrations at Rainhill, scene of the celebrated 'Rainhill Trials' from which *Rocket* emerged triumphant. I managed to snap a few locomotives in the cavalcade, together with the other hundreds of spectators in the stands, so here's a quiz to test your knowledge of our railway heritage!

The replica *Sans Pareil* had to be hauled past by a diesel shunter, but managed to return under her own steam.

1   Who was her builder?

2   Why, strictly speaking, was *Sans Pareil* ineligible for the prize at Rainhill in 1829?

LNWR 0-6-2T No 1054 dates from 1888.

5   What was the name applied to this class of locomotive?

6   Where is No 1054 normally to be seen?

Lion, the only original surviving locomotive of the Liverpool & Manchester Railway.

3   In what year was it built?

4   What boiler pressure does it work at?

Midland Railway No 673

7   What nickname was given to these MR 'singles'?

8   Who was their designer?

GWR No 5051 *Drysllwyn Castle*

9 *Drysllwyn Castle* was not the locomotive's name when it was withdrawn in 1963. What was it?

10 Which preservation group did 5051 represent at Rainhill?

Maunsell's 'Schools' Class No 925 *Cheltenham*

11 Which restricted-gauge line were the 'Schools' Class originally built to operate?

12 How many cylinders does *Cheltenham* have?

'Merchant Navy' 'Pacific' *Clan Line*

13 On one occasion, *Clan Line* attained an authenticated speed of over 100 mph near Axminster. What was the exact speed?

14 *Clan Line* was originally built with a streamlined casing. Which other important feature was also changed during the 1950s?

Gresley 'A4' 'Pacific' No 4498

15 Why was this locomotive in particular named after its designer?

16 What was the locomotive's BR number?

One of the well-loved 'Western' diesel-hydraulics

17 What class number did the 'Westerns' become?

18 Besides the familiar maroon, 'Westerns' were also seen in other distinctive liveries. Name one.

The ill-fated prototype APT

19 The APT-P sets comprised two power cars and how many trailers?

20 The APT was expected to knock 50 minutes off the London-Glasgow timings. What was the new journey time to be?

Across

1 Principal Midland Railway locomotive works . . . (5)

4 . . . and the Midland's first Locomotive Engineer (7)

7 Suffolk terminus of a short GER branch from Mellis (3)

9 Midland/GWR junction north-east of Bristol (4)

11 Midland station south of Ashchurch, but a Grange and an Abbey on the GWR! (6)

12 See 14

13 Whitemoor or Wath, perhaps (4)

14 and 12 Oil power! Name given to 47379 in 1986 (5,6)

17 A loop on a single line allows trains to do this (4)

18 Racing Downs — an LB&SCR terminus (5)

20 Magician gracing Nos 60027 and 73080 (6)

21 Nickname for a train-spotter (6)

22 American restaurant car? (5)

24 15-inch gauge steam railway, opened in 1927 (1,1,1,1)

25 Numbers on a signal box lever number plate indicating the sequence in which other levers should be pulled first (5)

28 What the LC&DR and the SER became in 1899 (1,1,1,1)

29 See 35

30 Device on a locomotive to assist adhesion (6)

31 Such a station has no ticket-collecting staff (4)

33 Post held by Fairburn on the LMS from 1944 to 1945 (1,1,1)

34 Military rank held by Sir Brian Robertson, Chairman of the BTC 1953-62 (7)

35 and 29 Brunel's Saltash bridge (5,6)

Down

1 Headquarters of the Great Western Society (6)

2 'Christian name' of No 70006 (6)

3 Town served by Town and Pen Mill stations (6)

4 Device for securing a rail in a chair (3)

5 River crossed by the Royal Border Bridge (5)

6 D1000, *Western* —— (10)

8 How 125 mph is described? (4,5)

10 Locomotive Superintendent of the LSWR, 1878-95 (5)

15 LNWR West Coast Main Line station in Westmoreland, junction for Windermere (9)

16 Uncomplimentary nickname for Edinburgh carried by LNER 'A1' 'Pacific' No 60160 (4,6)

18 See 26

19 In short, a modern 'non-stop' power station coal train (1,1,1)

23 Recess in a wall, such as might be provided for platelayers in a tunnel (5)

25 Unsuccessful Bulleid design of 'diesel lookalike' steam tank engine (6)

26 and 18 GER station south of Cambridge, junction for the Bartlow branch (6,3)

27 Form taken by the nameplates of the SR's 'West Country' 'Pacifics' (6)

28 —— Works Junction, at the foot of the Lickey incline (5)

32 BR's road delivery and collection operation, a subsidiary of the National Freight Corporation created in 1968 (1,1,1)

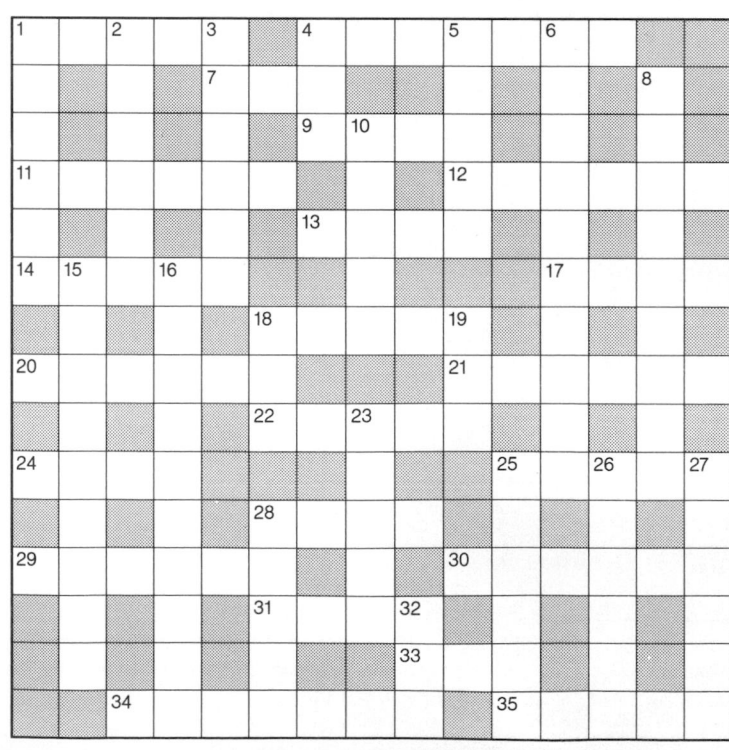

PICTURE THE SCENE
THE MENAI BRIDGE

In July 1974, when this picture was taken, the Menai Bridge was still undergoing reconstruction following the disaster of 1970.

1 What was the nature and cause of the 1970 tragedy?

2 For which railway company, predecessor of the LNWR, was the bridge built?

3 Which engineer was responsible for the adjacent road suspension bridge?

4 Which nearby bridge acted as a test of the practicality of the proposed Menai crossing?

5 Why did the strait have to be crossed with only two spans?

6 Which other prominent engineer gave encouragement to the Menai Bridge's designer as the spans were raised into position?

7 Complete the inscription on the stone in the foreground to discover the designer of the bridge.

8 What is the more correct name of the bridge?

9 What kind of animals guard the entrance to the bridge?

10 What feature was added to the bridge in 1980?

BRIDGES ...

While we're on the subject . . .

1   What is significant about the Gaunless bridge preserved at the NRM?

2   Three members of the consortium formed to build the Forth Bridge were the North British, North Eastern and Great Northern railways. Which was the other?

3   Only two all-metal viaducts survive on BR. One is Bennerley at Ilkeston, and the other is on the former LSWR in Devon. What is its name?

4   Glenfinnan viaduct on the West Highland Extension line was a British first — in what respect?

5   What do Drygrange viaduct, Shankend viaduct and Dunglass viaduct have in common?

6   Harringworth viaduct in Northants is Britain's longest. How many arches does it have?

7   In 1839 Brunel built a bridge with 'the flattest brick arches in the world'. Where was it, and which river did it span?

8   Which viaduct of the London to Brighton line is famous for its flanking Italianate pavilions and pierced piers?

9   On the opening of his Royal Border Bridge, Robert Stephenson was made an offer by Queen Victoria, but declined. What was the offer?

10 Which bridge included the infamous 'high girders'?

Picture question 1: Which bridge is this, seen in 1879, the year of its opening?

11 Where on the East Coast Main Line is Digswell viaduct?

12 On which line are the two steel viaducts on Horseshoe Bend?

13 Three modes of transport are involved in Brunel's triple Windmill bridge at Southall, Middlesex — which, and in what order?

14 What kind of bridge crossed the Dee estuary at Harrowden?

15 Which famous Welsh bridge has suffered severe attack by the Teredo worm?

16 There was only one timber bridge on the original GWR main line — where was it?

17 Which river is crossed by the well-known picturesque viaduct at Knaresborough, Yorks?

Picture question 2: Who opened Brunel's Saltash bridge?

. . . AND TUNNELS

1 Where is Shakespeare Tunnel?

2 Which station's operation was hampered by an exit up the 1 in 42 tunnel of Cowlairs Incline?

3 Higham Tunnel near Strood was shared in the 1840s by a railway and what other form of transport?

4 What were the original Woodhead tunnels used to carry under the Pennines when they were closed to rail traffic?

5 Which major Yorkshire tunnel was built using a parallel, lower canal tunnel connected by adits to transport materials?

6 Which tunnel was inundated by the Great Spring during construction, and is still being pumped out?

7 Which tunnel built in 1841 for the Manchester & Leeds Railway was then the world's longest?

8 A miniature version of which tunnel's northern portal, in Otley churchyard, forms a memorial to the men who died during its construction?

9 Which is the deepest and longest tunnel on the Settle & Carlisle line?

10 Which tunnel on the London and Brighton line has an inhabited cottage perched between the towers of the northern portal?

11 Part of which London underground line forms the world's longest tunnel, at 17 miles?

12 With what aspect of tunnelling is James Greathead associated?

13 Which Staffordshire tunnel entrance was highly ornamented at the demand of the Earl of Lichfield, through whose estate the railway ran?

Picture question: Which portal of Box tunnel is this — east or west?

14 How many individual bores are there comprising Primrose Hill Tunnels outside Euston?

15 On which famous stretch of line do Kennaway, Coryton, Phillot, Clerks and Parsons tunnels occur within less than 1½ miles?

16 On which line were Devonshire, Chilcompton and Winsor Hill tunnels to be found?

17 Which railway company built Catesby tunnel?

18 During the Second World War, one Midland line named express train ran through more tunnels on its route than any other in British history — which?

19 Which Midlands joint station was flanked by Mansfield Road and Victoria Street tunnels?

FROM THE TRAIN

Before we pass from the bridges and tunnels to the inclines, let's take a breather with an easy pictorial puzzle. All you have to do is identify the locations of these three photographs.

From bridges and tunnels to inclines, so beloved of photographers, where the sounds of the steam age were heard to their best advantage!

INCLINES

1 On which incline was Scout Green signal box situated?

2 By what name is the 15 miles of the Settle & Carlisle line at almost a constant 1 in 100 gradient often referred to?

3 On which incline did the unique locomotive No 58100 operate?

4 Which summit is higher above sea level — Shap or Beattock?

5 Part of the GWR's South Devon line is very briefly steeper than Lickey. What is the gradient, and which bank does it form a part of?

6 Which incline north of Bury included 5 miles continuously at between 1 in 66 and 1 in 81?

7 On which bank was the picturesquely named Upwey Wishing Well Halt situated?

8 What is the name of the summit of the Somerset & Dorset line between Radstock and Shepton Mallet?

9 Mortehoe stands at the summit of a two-mile 1 in 36 climb from which seaside resort terminus?

10 Which MR Peak District tunnel has the whole of its 1¾-mile length on a gradient of 1 in 90?

11 The London-bound South Devon bank between Plymouth and Totnes is Hermerdon, but what is the name of the opposite Plymouth-bound incline?

12 On which bank, and which line, was Steele Road an intermediate station, midway up nearly 8 miles at 1 in 75?

13 From which London terminus were trains hauled by endless rope from 1837 to 1844?

14 From which principal city did Miles Platting bank provide a severe north-west-bound exit?

15 What is the name of the station at the summit of the long incline on the Caledonian line between Edinburgh and Carstairs?

16 On which line is Glenoglehead bank and summit?

17 Which is Britain's longest tunnel on a constant, continual rising gradient?

18 Box Tunnel is built on a continuous rising gradient, the steepest between Paddington and Bristol. What is it?

19 Which year saw the last regular passenger train booked for banking assistance up the Lickey Incline?

Picture question: Which summit, which gives its name to the signal box and passing place seen here in 1970, is reached after a 28-mile climb from Fort William during which the line climbs from sea level to 1,350 feet?

THE SETTLE AND CARLISLE

No consideration of bridges, tunnels and inclines would be complete without some reference to the Settle & Carlisle line. After all, the story goes that the railway's surveyors were informed by a local farmer that there wasn't enough level ground between the two places to build a house, let alone a railway. How well do you know your Settle & Carlisle . . .?

1   The line possessed what were said to be the highest water troughs in the world. Where were they situated?

2   What was the name of the signal box between Dent and Blea Moor?

3   What is the alternative name of Ribblehead viaduct . . .?

4   . . . and what river does it cross?

5   Which river valley is followed by the line between Ais Gill and Carlisle?

6   Which other pre-Grouping company had stations at both Appleby and Kirkby Stephen?

7   Stations are often remote from the communities they serve; one is 4 miles away and 600 feet higher than the place whose name it takes. Which?

8   To whom is there a memorial plaque on Appleby station?

Picture question 1: What was the former name of Garsdale station?

9   What, in connection with the building of the line, were Jericho, Belgravia, Salt Lake City and Batty Green?

10   Why was Garsdale turntable built within a sleeper 'stockade'?

11   The line includes Britain's highest main-line tunnel. Which is it?

12   Dandry Mire viaduct was not planned — so why did it have to be built?

13   Which of the line's viaducts, at 165 feet high, was alleged to be the tallest on the Midland Railway's system?

14   With which placename was Lazonby paired in the station name?

15   In Blea Moor tunnel, the line crosses the boundary between North Yorkshire and which other county?

16   In what year were local services withdrawn from the route?

17   What kind of installation is to be found at Low House, near Armathwaite?

18   What kind of structure bears the name Lunds?

19   The 'Farewell to Steam' railtour traversed the route in August 1968. How many years was it before steam returned once more to the Settle & Carlisle route?

Picture question 2: This is Dent station. It holds the record for an English main-line station — what is it?

GRADIENT PROFILE

Finally on the subject of inclines, fill in the answers to the following clues in the appropriate column of the 'gradient profile' to read downwards. When all the words are in place, the shaded squares will spell out the name of the highest summit level on British railways, between Perth and Inverness.

1 Summit and tunnel on the trans-Pennine former Great Central route (8)

2 Summit on the S&DJR between Radstock and Shepton Mallet (7)

3 Summit on the West Highland line between Tulloch and the answer to no 7 (7)

4 Summit on the same line north of Crianlarich (7)

5 Tunnel and banks on the South Devon main line of the GWR between Newton Abbot and Totnes (7)

6 Bank on the West Coast Main Line north of Carlisle (8)

7 Passing place between answers 3 and 4 — once 'Britain's loneliest signal box' (7)

8 Bank and tunnel on the Great Western main line between Yeovil and Maiden Newton (8)

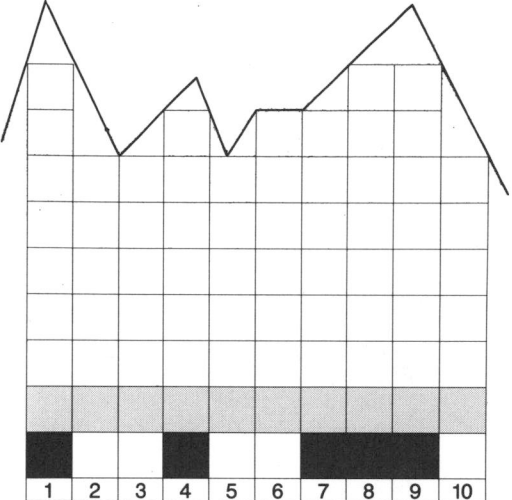

9 Tunnel and summit on the Waverley Route between Riccarton and Hawick (8)

10 Another of the GWR's South Devon banks, between Totnes and Brent (7)

MORE MARSHALLING

See page 35 for how to solve this puzzle.

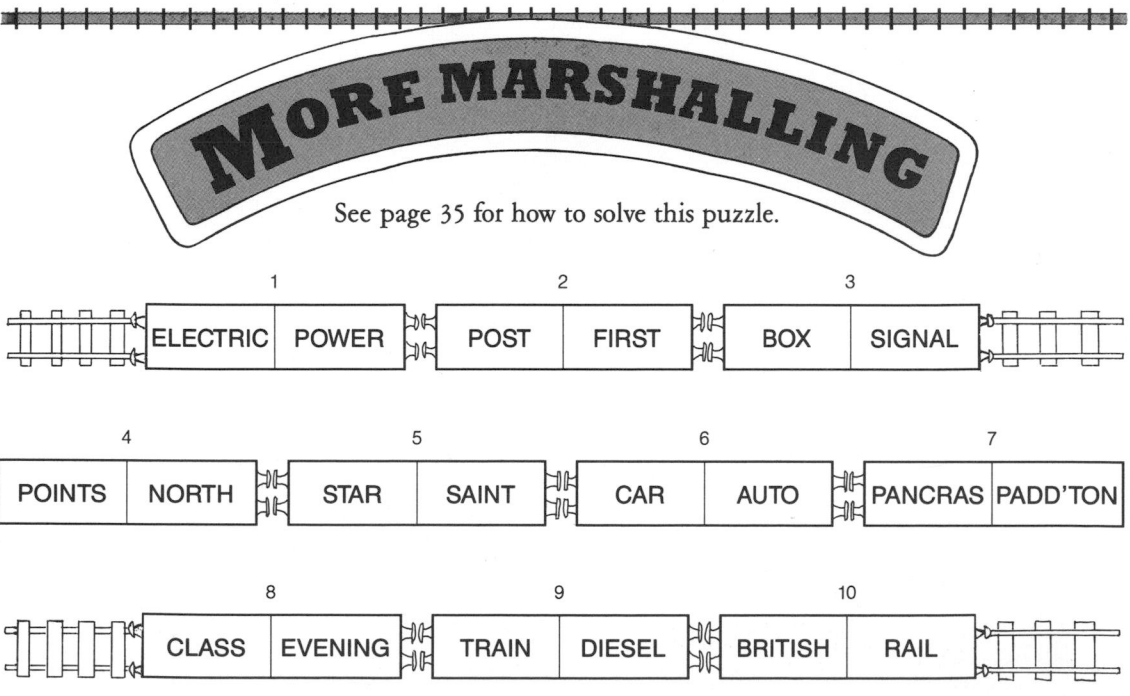

1 ELECTRIC | POWER — POST | FIRST — BOX | SIGNAL

4 POINTS | NORTH — 5 STAR | SAINT — 6 CAR | AUTO — 7 PANCRAS | PADD'TON

8 CLASS | EVENING — 9 TRAIN | DIESEL — 10 BRITISH | RAIL

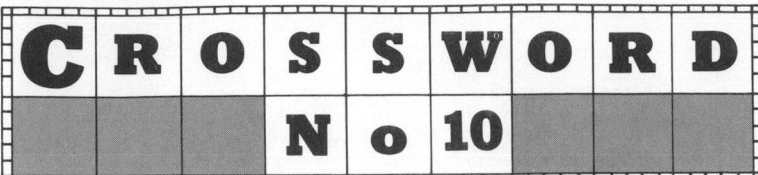
Across

1 and 4 Incline immediately outside Euston station (6,4)

6 Northern Ireland Railway operated by the LMS (1,1,1)

8 Colour borne by both a locomotive and train of the LNER on its augural run in September 1935 (6)

10 Triangular junction north of Leicester on the Midland main line (6)

11 and 16 Anything less than 4'8½"! (6,5)

12 The only surviving original locomotive of the Liverpool & Manchester Railway (4)

13 Such cylinders are found between the frames (6)

14 Forty-arch viaduct (and notorious bottleneck) on the GNR main line in Herts (6)

15 Railway of which Wainwright and Maunsell were 32 across (1,1,1,1)

16 See 11

17 New —— Yard Junction, former signal box just outside London's Broad Street (3)

18 'Britannia' 46 (5)

21 Type of ground signal (4)

24 Northamptonshire town served by the Midland's Kettering-Huntingdon branch (6)

25 D600 (6)

26 '—— and spilt milk' — one description of the LNWR carriage livery (4)

27 Term applied to a locomotive with only one pair of driving wheels (6)

29 Alternative name for a single line token (6)

31 Sir —— Watkin, Chairman of the SER, MS&LR, Metropolitan and the first Channel Tunnel company (6)

32 Alternative title for a company's Locomotive Engineer (1,1,1)

33 Surname of the Colonel who designed the GCR's hotel at Marylebone, later BRB headquarters (4)

34 Britain's longest railway tunnel (6)

Down

1 Buildings with which Earls, World War 2 aircraft and Abbeys were associated on the GWR! (7)

2 Norfolk station at the hub of the M&GNR system (6,9)

3 —— Valley Junction, at the foot of the northbound descent from Shap, near Penrith (4)

4 Headquarters of the Furness Railway (6-2-7)

5 Mr Annett patented one for releasing levers at outlying ground frames (3)

6 Metropolitan/District Railway station between Paddington and High Street Kensington (7,4,4)

7 —— Ferry Bridge, crossing Loch Etive on the Caledonian's Ballachulish line (6)

9 Sir Vincent ——, 32 across of the NER, 1910-22 (5)

10 Type of bridge found at Selby and Naburn (5)

19 Device which often adorned a titled train's headboard (5)

20 Station near the summit of the Midland's Hope Valley line (5)

22 GWR bank and tunnel between Moreton-in-Marsh and Honeybourne — sounds as though it's related to 1 and 4 across! (7)

23 Name given to the 4-6-4T wheel arrangement (6)

28 —— Hill, historic Liverpool station restored for the Rocket 150 celebrations in 1980 (4)

30 River valley followed by the GWR's line from Stoke Canon to Morebath Junction (3)

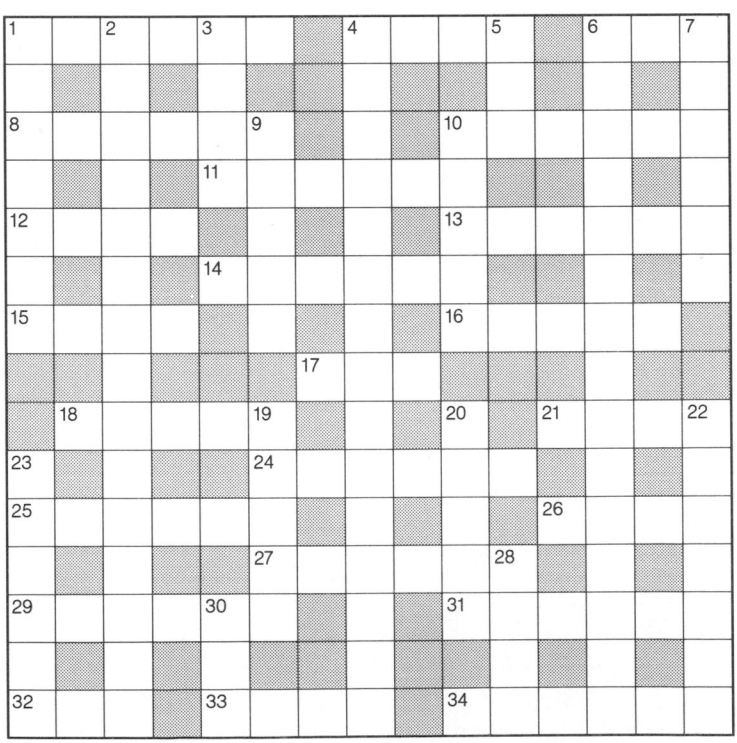

MIXED GOODS

Which is the odd one out in each of these groups?

1 Exeter, Salisbury, Andover, Shaftesbury

2 North Western, North Eastern, South Eastern, South Western

3 Foregate Street, Snow Hill, New Street, Moor Street

4 *Wightwick Hall, Swanage, Duchess of Hamilton, Duke of Gloucester*

5 Churchward, Gresley, Walschaerts, Stephenson

6 Pullman, Hawksworth, Hudson, Stephenson

7 'A1s' 60113-60162, 'A3s' 60035-60112, 'A4s' 60001-60034

8 Uxbridge, Chesham, Stanmore, Watford

9 Stour, Wye, Severn, Colne

10 George, William, Frederick, Augustus

11 Stanier, Gresley, Bulleid, Fowler

12 Central, Eastern, Northern, Junction

13 Lord Nelson, Dreadnaught, Alfred the Great, Teutonic

14 Lincolnshire, Manchester, Yorkshire, Sheffield

15 Evening, Morning, Rising, Afternoon

16 Coronation, Cornish Riviera, Flying Scotsman, Royal Scot

17 Bassenthwaite, Ullswater, Windermere, Coniston

18 Caledonian, Midland, Cambrian, Furness

19 Royal Border Bridge, Tay Bridge, Forth Bridge, Severn Bridge

20 *Mauretania, Titanic, Lusitania, Aquitania*

THE STATELY HOMES OF ENGLAND

(. . . and Wales, of course!) Halls, Manors, Granges, Castles — these stately buildings provided the names for hundreds of GWR steam locomotives. But of those listed below, which was which? (One is a 'red herring', and one was named after both a Hall and a Castle — can you spot them?)

1 Pendennis

2 Capel Dewi

3 Llanthony

4 Cookham

5 Hinton

6 Dumbleton

7 Lydham

8 Hagley

9 Crynant

10 Broughton

THE PRESERVATION SCENE II

Many 'Halls' and 'Manors' have, happily, found themselves rescued, restored and running on the preserved lines up and down the country. Here's a further collection of questions to test your knowledge of our steam railways.

Picture question: Which pre-Grouping company operated this line, and by what name is it now known?

1   The preservation of which LMS locomotive formed the start of the Dinting Railway Centre?

2   Who was the engineer of the original North Yorkshire Moors Railway between Whitby and Pickering?

3   Why is it appropriate that the NYMR's 'Black Five' No 4767 should have been named *George Stephenson*?

4   On which preserved line is Mytholmes tunnel to be found?

5   Where was the original Museum of British Transport established, the germ of the present NRM?

6   Which northern preserved line incorporates part of a route established in 1758 by the first Act of Parliament sanctioning the building of a railway?

7   In what kind of industrial installation had the Strathspey Railway's 'Pug' *Dailuaine* formerly worked?

8   On which line can the longest single journey on a British preserved railway be made?

9   The Rother Valley Light Railway of 1900 is now known under a different name. What is it?

10 What kind of industrial complex is the site of the Sittingbourne to Kemsley Light Railway?

11 Which well-known company currently plays host to *Princess Elizabeth*?

12 Which preservation centre is split in half by the still-used goods-only BR Aylesbury-Bletchley line?

13 In the preservation field, what do the initials ARPS stand for?

14 What collective name has been applied to the preserved Welsh narrow gauge railways by their joint marketing board?

15 Why were Festiniog Railway steam locomotives converted from coal to oil burning?

16 Which company operated both the Vale of Rheidol Railway and the Welshpool and Llanfair Light Railway in the early years of this century?

17 Which preserved narrow gauge line was opened in 1876, declared bankrupt in 1877, completely abandoned in 1912, and has been in the hands of private operators since 1915?

18 Who originally bought 4472 *Flying Scotsman* from BR in 1963 and owned her for ten years?

19 Which station is the headquarters of the Keighley & Worth Valley Railway?

BARRY

And of course a great number of preserved locomotives came from that extraordinary 'graveyard of steam', Woodhams' scrapyard at Barry in South Wales. These three pictures were taken in the autumn of 1968; the better two were taken by my friend Richard Bird on a school Railway Society trip.

1 In which year did the first of the withdrawn locomotives to be subsequently rescued arrive at Woodhams'?

2 What distinction is held by ex-MR 0-6-0 No 43924, which arrived at Barry in 1965?

3 When GWR 0-6-2T No 6619 arrived at Barry in 1963 it was as a working locomotive, shunting condemned engines. Why did it stay there for over 11 years?

4 In 1980, Dai Woodham and others formed the 'Barry 21 Club' to rescue as many as possible of the remaining engines. Which author and railway enthusiast MP was also a prominent member of the Club?

5 Only one LNER locomotive graced Woodhams' yard. What class was it?

Rusting in the rain was LMS 2-8-0 No 53808.

6 This locomotive and its fellows were built specifically to work one particular line. Which?

7 At which shed on that line did No 53808 spend all of its nearly 40 years' working life?

8 No 53808 was only the ninth engine to be rescued from Barry, in 1970. Which West Country preserved line took delivery of the locomotive in 1976?

Its rear driving wheels already scathed by the cutter's torch, GWR 'King' No 6024 *King Edward I* seemed destined never to run again . . . yet has recently returned to steam.

9 Who was the locomotive's designer?

10 The most powerful 4-6-0s ever built in this country, they were the first to operate at such a high boiler pressure. What was the pressure?

11 When withdrawn in 1962, No 6024 and its companion behind were sold to a scrapyard in Briton Ferry near Neath. Why did they end up at Barry, a fact that 'saved their lives'?

Another 'King' — 'Jinty' No 47406 — dubbed 'King of Edge Hill' by a passing admirer — waits in the setting sun at the end of the line.

12 Nine 'Jinties' have been preserved in all. How many of these nine were rescued from Barry?

13 Where was Edge Hill shed, and at which of the same city's stations did No 47406 end her days on pilot duty?

THE BIG FOUR III: GWR

1 Which GWR constituent at the 1923 Grouping had the most locomotives and carriages after the GWR itself?

2 The GWR's only electrified lines were as a result of its part ownership of which surburban line?

3 On which route were the GWR's first diesel railcars introduced in 1933?

4 What experiment was tried on *King Henry VII* and *Manorbier Castle* in 1935?

5 A new GWR holiday facility first appeared at Easter 1934. What was it?

6 With the doubling of the Scorrier-Redruth section in 1931, there remained only one stretch of single line between Paddington and Penzance. Where was it?

7 Two 'cut-off' avoiding lines on the West of England main line were opened in 1932. One was at Frome; where was the other?

8 Which new locomotive was the GWR's exhibit at the 1924 British Empire Exhibition at Wembley?

9 In 1924, the new 'Castle' Class 4-6-0 *Viscount Churchill* appeared, having been rebuilt from a previous notable locomotive. Which?

10 Which GWR locomotive appeared at the Fair of the Iron Horse in the USA, marking the centenary of the Baltimore & Ohio Railroad in 1927?

11 The junction of the GWR's two main lines to the West, from London and the Midlands, near Taunton was provided with a flyover junction in the 1930s. What was the name of the junction?

12 Collegewood was the last of what kind of original structure to be replaced by the GWR, in 1934-5?

13 Which train established a record in 1932 with an average speed of 81.7 mph which remained unbroken for 20 years?

14 The GWR had a fine safety record; in 1936, one passenger was killed in the Shrivenham crash. How many passengers had died in accidents on the GWR in the previous 20 years?

15 The GWR was the world's largest owner of what type of facility in the 1920s?

16 At which resort was the GWR-owned hotel, the Tregenna Castle?

17 Class 'S160' 2-8-0 No 1604 was involved in a ceremony at Paddington in December 1942. What was the occasion?

18 Which LMS-designed locomotive was built in considerable numbers at Swindon between 1943 and 1945?

19 In 1940, the GWR raised £5,000 for the purchase of a certain item to help the war effort, and named 'Castle' No 5071 after it to mark the achievement. What was the item?

20 The first of the post-war 'Castles' in the new 70XX number range was named after the last Chairman of the GWR. Who was he?

21 Which cartoonist was commissioned to produce *Railway Ribaldry* for the GWR's centenary in 1935?

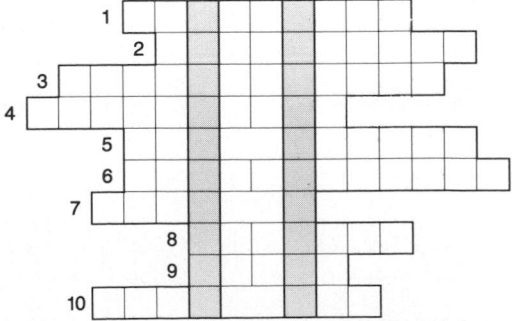

DOWN EXPRESS

SLIP COACHES II

See page 39 for how to solve this puzzle. In this example, the lower grid will spell out a line from a chapter on slip coaches in the GWR's *The 10.30 Limited*. Bold lines indicate breaks between words.

Clues

1 Nickname given to an early type of 3rd class carriage (8)

2 'Warship' D824 (9)

3 Pre-Grouping railway company whose main line ran from Carlisle to Aberdeen (10)

4 Wilson and T.W., engineer brothers (8)

5 CME of the LNER from 1946 (10)

6 —— *Abbey*, No 5091, or —— *Grange*, No 6850 (6)

7 Shed 10F, near Burnley, one of the last steam sheds (4,5)

8 No 60009, *Union of South* —— (6)

9 Station and junction on the SE&CR main line to Dover (9)

10 Name adopted by BR for its main-line passenger business (5-4)

11 Mr Cook or Mr Edmondson, perhaps (6)

12 Railway having a main line from Carnforth to Whitehaven (7)

13 Locomotive Engineer of the LB&SCR, 1870-89 (9)

14 Sixteenth-century English navigator remembered by 'Jubilee' No 45640 and 'Lord Nelson' No 30864 (8)

15 Swindon goods station on the M&SWJR (6,5)

16 Midlands spa town with parallel GWR and LNWR stations (10)

17 Locomotive works of the Great North of Scotland Railway (9)

18 Special passenger vehicles first introduced into Britain (on the MR) in 1874 (7,4)

19 Type of tank engine with water tanks on either side of the boiler above the running plate (7)

20 125 mph? (4,5)

The clues in this puzzle are all connected with express trains. When all the answers are in place, the two shaded columns will spell out the stations at either end of the route of 'The World's Fastest Train' in the early 1920s.

1 Departure station of the down 'Thames-Clyde Express' (2,7)

2 Destination of the down 'Mancunian' (10)

3 Name given to an overnight container train between London and clue 2 introduced in 1963 (12)

4 Buildings common to Hereford, Worcester and Oxford which gave their name to an express to those places (10)

5 Express introduced on the GWR main line in 1935 to celebrate the route's centenary (10)

6 The S&D's most famous named train (5,7)

7 'Red' express between London and Carmarthen (6)

8 Time taken by LMS London-Birmingham expresses that became the name by which they were known (3-4)

9 '—— Mails', the train being hauled by *City of Truro* when the controversial 102.4 mph was claimed (5)

10 Euston-Inverness express via Birmingham and Wolverhampton, introduced in 1976 (8)

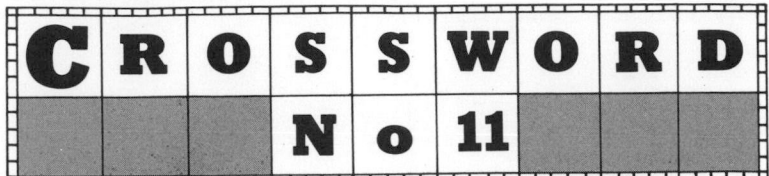
Across

1 Wood used to give the characteristic finish to LNER coaches (4)

7 Hull goods station and former engine shed (11)

8 St Davids or St Thomas (6)

9 Former principal Birmingham station of the GWR (4,4)

11 and 12 Brunel was famous for his 'stovepipe' example! (3,3)

14 'Britannia' 46 (5)

17 Station at the end of the preserved Strathspey Railway (8)

20 The GWR's Adlestrop station inspired one (4)

21 —— *Patricia*, 'Princess Royal' No 46210 (4)

23 Antipodean territory marked by 'Jubilee' No 45569 (8)

27 Bridge of ——, station on the West Highland line (5)

28 Former colour of distant signal arms (3)

29 Symonds ——, beauty spot served by the GWR's Monmouth-Ross line (3)

30 Warship name originally carried by 'Jubilee' No 45728, and more recently by 50049 (8)

32 London Square served by the Metropolitan/District line (6)

33 D1 (7,4)

34 What Geoffrey Freeman Allen once did on *Modern Railways* (4)

Down

1 Line serving Nuneaton, Lichfield and Rugeley (5,6)

2 Midland Railway hotel of 1912 adjoining Liverpool Central (7)

3 GWR West of England junction for the Newquay line (3)

4 Wellington was such a Duke! (4)

5 Style of architecture exemplified superbly by St Pancras station (6)

6 Item presented to *King George V* at the Baltimore & Ohio Railroad centenary celebrations (4)

7 Bucks Golf Club served by its own halt on the GW&GC joint line (6)

9 GWR class of 4-6-0s (4)

10 Familiar expression for a railway engine (4)

13 Item lacking in an open carriage! (11)

15 Welsh town linked with Brecon by railway (5)

16 Parts of semaphore signals (4)

18 GER station and junction in north Cambs (3)

19 GWR Junction across the Severn from Gloucester (4)

20 Company that ran the London dockland railway to Gallions (1,1,1)

22 GN of S junction station north of Aberdeen (4)

24 Lancaster Green —— (4)

25 —— Hill Tunnel, just west of Box Tunnel (6)

26 One of the two termini of the GWR Pembrokeshire branch from Clarbeston Road (7)

27 First name of Alan Bloom's 'Britannia' (6)

30 Name given by the Rev Awdry to the ex-GWR 0-6-0 pannier tank in the Railway Stories (4)

31 ——hold Junction, Haywards Heath, LB&SCR (4)

32 Ideal background against which to sight a semaphore signal (3)

PICTURE THE SCENE

IN THE BOX

This picture was taken during a visit to Wellingborough area signal boxes in August 1983. Finedon Road, together with all the others in the district, closed in December 1987 as the line came under the control of Leicester panel.

1 The block instrument nearest the camera is a standard BR 'three position' instrument. What are the three positions indicated by the needle?

2 The lever reversed in the frame in the foreground is in its normal position and is painted blue. What is its function?

3 The dials on the front of the block shelf repeat the aspects of signals out of the signalman's sight as 'OFF' or 'ON', but what is the intermediate indication when an arm has not fully cleared or returned?

4 What colour are levers operating points?

5 Finedon Road box stands on the up side of the line, and the signalman stands with his back to the main line to operate the frame. At which end of the frame as he looks at it will the principal down line signals be?

6 What is the function of a lever painted with black and white chevrons pointing downwards?

7 What is the difference between a 'pegging' and a 'non-pegging' block instrument?

8 The Board of Trade stipulated that mechanically operated points should normally be no more than how many yards from the operating signal box?

9 Before a signalman can accept a train, the line to a certain 'clearing point' beyond the outermost home signal must be clear. Under usual circumstances, how far beyond the signal is the clearing point?

10 What is the standard BR bell code for an express passenger train?

I photographed this ex-GWR signal box in 1970, not so much because it was anywhere particularly interesting, but because of the length of its nameplate! The GWR was always very keen to let you know exactly where you were. To discover the missing five words, answer the clues and enter the answers in the grid, reading downwards. The letters in the two 'nameplates' will spell out the box's name.

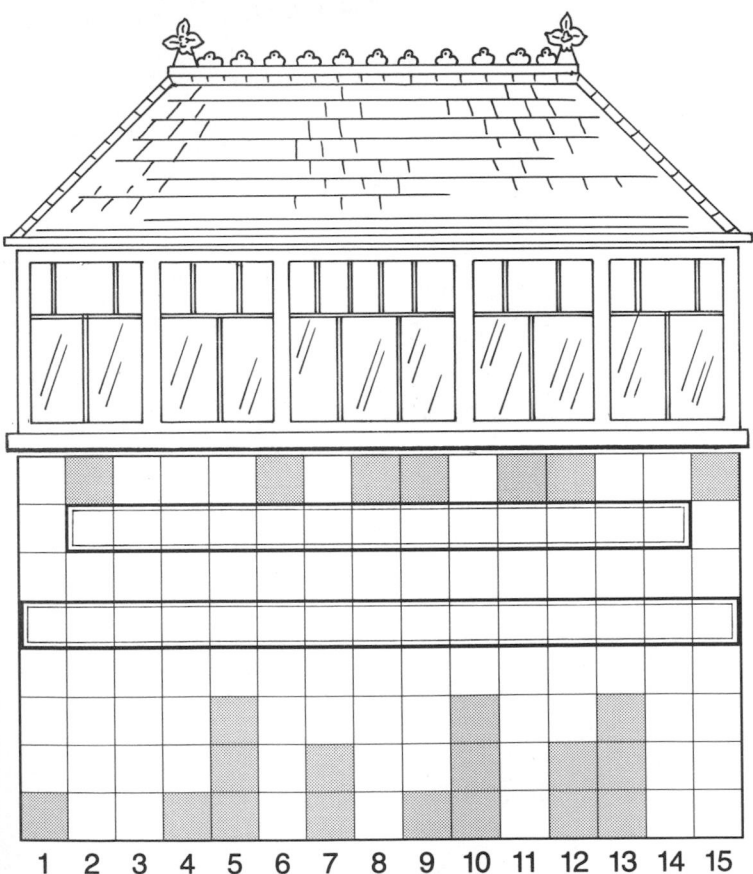

Clues

1 Name of the Junction between the LB&SCR and SE&CR between Sydenham and answer 8 (7)

2 Perhaps Britain's most famous junction! (7)

3 Junction south of Guildford between the LSWR and SE&CR Dorking and Redhill lines (8)

4 GNR junction between Grantham and Nottingham named after a local village, Vale and castle (7)

5 GWR junction south of Newton Abbot . . . (5)

6 . . . for this Devon seaside resort (7)

7 Junction in rural Bucks, northern outpost of the Metropolitan Railway on the LNWR Bletchley-Oxford line (6)

8 South London station and complex of junctions on the LB&SCR Brighton line (7)

9 Three-way junction at the hub of the Birkenhead Joint Railway (6)

10 —— Junction, end-on junction between the NBR and NER in Carlisle (5)

11 Stratford-on-Avon & —— Junction Railway (7)

12 —— Stores Junction, part of the Trent Junctions complex on the answer 11 Railway (5)

13 —— Bridge, NBR junction station for the Fort Augustus branch (5)

14 Principal station in the town where the pictured signal box was situated (8)

15 East Coast Main Line junction station that includes a railway level crossing (7)

LEVER LEADS I

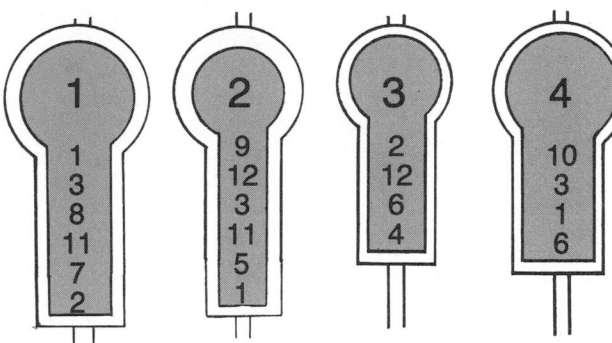

Moving right along with our current signalling theme, below are four signal box lever plates numbered 1 to 4, each showing the 'leads', the subsidiary numbers indicating which order preceding levers should be reversed in the locking sequence to release the lever in question.

To find out what each of these levers operates, solve the signalling clues below, take the initial letter of each and rearrange them according to the order shown on the lever plate. For example the function of lever no 1 will be spelled out by the initial letters of the answers to clues 1, 3, 8, 11, 7 and 2.

Clues

1 Semaphore signal in advance of a signal box controlling the entrance to the section ahead (7)

2 One of the indications of a three position block instrument (4,5)

3 Term applied to signals, often automatic, situated between block posts to break up unduly long sections (12)

4 Junction at which the East and West Coast rivals converged northbound to Aberdeen in the Railway Races of 1895 (8)

5 Type of points inserted at the exit from a siding to guard against trains moving on to the main line (4)

6 Term applied to a pair of points connecting two parallel running lines (9)

7 Term applied to a further clue 1 signal beyond the first (8)

8 Usual name for a 'signal bridge' (6)

9 Name given to the type of block instrument with a commutator handle beneath the instrument face, for sending messages (6)

10 Warning signal, whether semaphore or colour light (7)

11 East Coast Main Line station in Yorkshire, one of four sites to pioneer route control signals on the LNER in 1939 (13)

12 Word usually used to describe a signal that is in the clear position (3)

JUNCTIONS

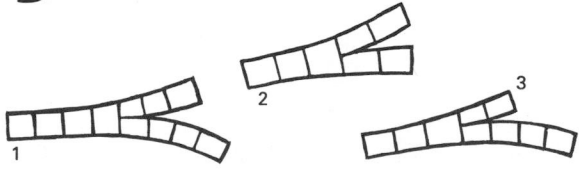

Yes, a further variation on the theme! Each clue leads to two answers with railway connections which each begin with the same letters, then 'diverge' into two separate words. Can you discover the pairs?

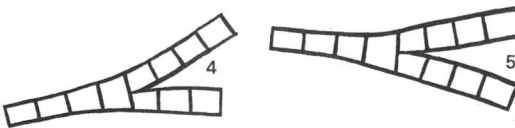

1 SR CME 1938-47 and a type of rail requiring chairs and keys

2 S&D Express and 'Deltic' 7

3 BRB Chairman 1971-6 and Minister of Transport of the early '60s

4 Light Railway Colonel and preserved 'Terrier' No 55

5 Timetable pioneer and Exchange terminus city

CHANGE FOR . . . ?

From the following diagrams, can you identify the name of each well-known junction or junction station at the centre of the map?

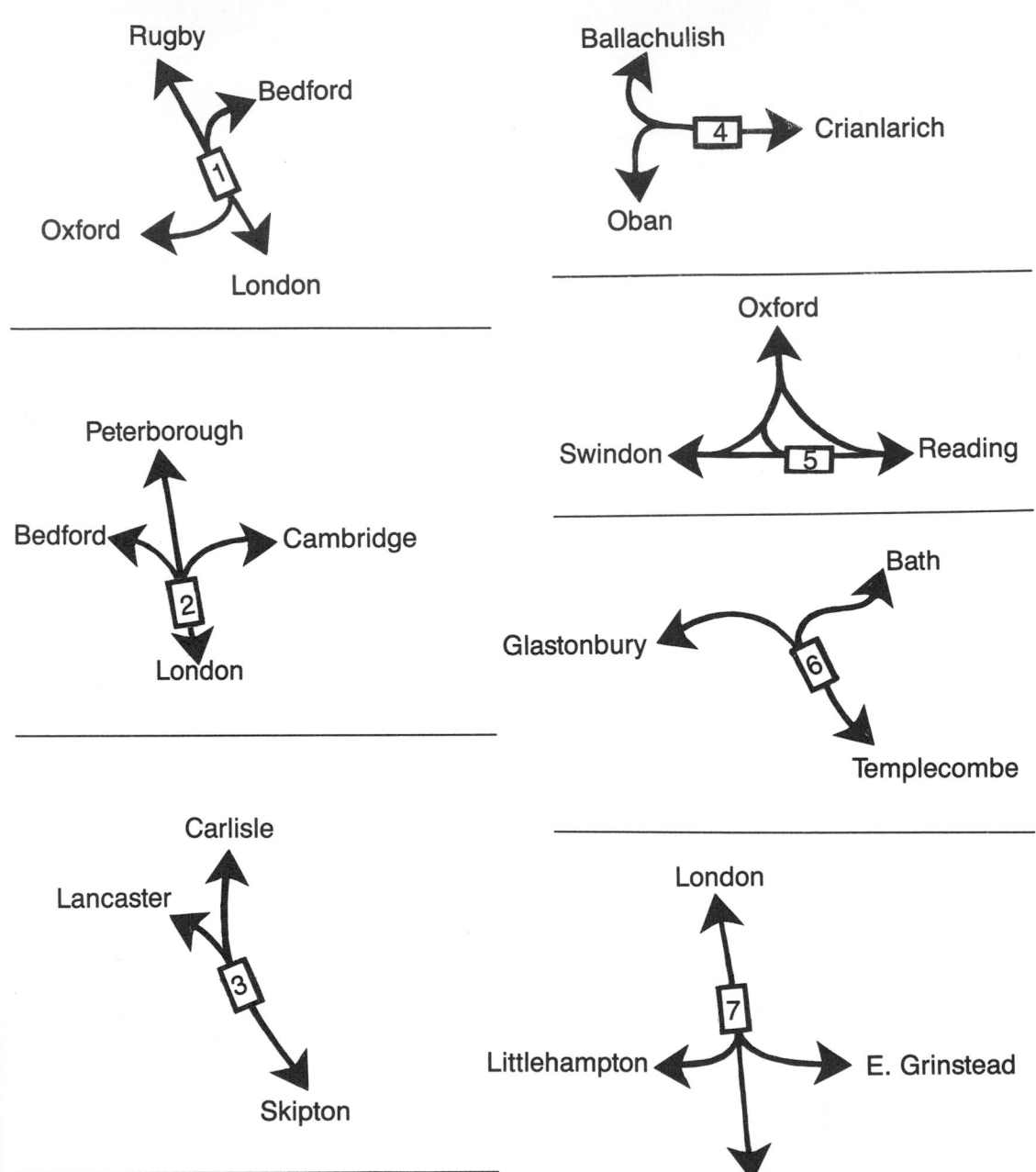

EMPTY STOCK II

See page 38 for how to solve this puzzle.

Across

2 Newton —— (5)
6 See picture clue
7 Cromford & —— Peak Railway (4)
8 —— 3 down (3)
9 Old —— Common (3)
10 Birmingham —— Hill (4)
12 —— Croydon (4)
14 —— signal (4)
18 —— Summit (4)
20 *Steady* —— (60513) (3)
21 Big —— (3)
22 —— Moor Tunnel (4)
23 —— & Manifold Valley Light Railway (4)
24 —— 9 across (Paddington) (5)

Down

1 —— Kings or Sisters (GER) (5)
2 'Golden ——' (5)
3 Vacuum —— (5)
4 —— Cocks Junction (5)
5 *Burton —— Hall* (5)
11 —.—.—. Bulleid (1,1,1)
13 ——pan (3)
15 *——borough* (D7) (5)
16 Line —— (5)
17 *St* —— (D9001) (5)
18 —— Heath (GWR) (5)
19 —— Mills Junctions (LT&S & GER) (5)

Picture clue: Valve —— (4)

PEOPLE

1 What was Sir Nigel Gresley's first name?

2 In 1986, 37425 was given a nameplate reading *Concrete Bob*, and another for the opposite side with that gentleman's real name. What is it?

3 Joseph, George, John, Joseph Jnr and R. J. all enjoyed high position on the GWR between 1864 and 1946. What was their surname?

4 How old was Sir William Stanier when he died in 1966?

5 Sir Thomas Bouch died in 1880 aged just 58. What event of the previous year led to his early death?

6 Who was responsible for the installation of Britain's first stationary locomotive testing plant at Swindon?

7 Who were the LNWR's 'Claughton' Class 4-6-0s named after?

8 What was the relationship between Dugald and Peter Drummond?

9 Of which railway was Sir Sam Fay the enterprising General Manager from 1902 to 1922?

10 Sir George Gibb, General Manager of the GER from 1891, resigned in 1906 to become Managing Director of which surburban railway system?

11 Who was known as the 'Railway King' in the 1840s?

12 For which company was Dr Beeching a Technical Director when he became a member of Marples' railway advisory group?

13 Which GWR General Manager left the company in 1929 to become Chairman of AEI?

14 What was the name of John Saxby's partner in the famous signalling company?

15 Which signalling pioneer patented his 'lock and block' system in 1875?

16 What nationality was George Westinghouse, of brake and signal fame?

17 This contractor built 17,000 route miles of line in Britain, 2,800 abroad, and at one time employed 45,000 men. Who was he?

18 Who was the Minister of Transport responsible for the important 1968 Transport Act?

19 Who travelled the country surveying the routes of his lines in the 'Flying Hearse'?

20 Sir Eric Geddes was the first to hold a new government post in 1919. Which?

CROSSWORD No 12

Across

2 SW Asian capital after which 'A2/3' 'Pacific' No 60518 was named (6)

7 CME of the LSWR 1912-22 (4)

8 GWR junction for the Windsor branch (6)

9 'Duchess' No 46234 (8)

10 Short extension of track beyond points for shunting etc (4)

12 Successor to Johnson as CME of the Midland Railway (6)

14 Liverpool in London, maybe! (6)

15 Terminus of a short GER branch from Mellis (3)

16 McKenzie & ——, manufacturers of signalling equipment (7)

19 Sussex town linked with Camber by tramway (3)

21 What had to be passed before a railway could be built (3)

22 Track packing material (7)

26 River bridged by Brunel at Chepstow (3)

28 Number of the RH&DR's *Black Prince*, or the Isle of Wight Steam Railway's 2 down *Newport* (6)

29 Arthurian Standard 4-6-0 No 73116 (6)

32 Device for locating and locking a facing point in position (4)

33 'Duchess' No 46229 (8)

35 Rainhill victor (6)

36 Throstle —— Junction, west of Manchester on the CLC (4)

37 Leaf or coil, perhaps (6)

Down

1 Nickname for the Horwich 2-6-0 designed by George Hughes (4)

2 Nickname for the LB&SCR 'A' Class 0-6-0 Stroudley tank engine (7)

3 Headquarters of the Keighley & Worth Valley Railway (7)

4 LB&SCR junction for the Littlehampton branch (7)

5 'The Old —— and ——', the Oxford, Worcester & Wolverhampton Railway's disparaging nickname! (5)

6 GCR London Extension station between Catesby Tunnel and Woodford Halse (10)

8 The '—— Bogies', 4-4-0s designed by David Jones to work the Highland's Kyle of Lochalsh line (4)

11 —— Wipe Junction, meeting of the GCR, GNR and GN&GE Joint at Lincoln (3)

13 River valley followed by the West Coast Main Line northwards towards Shap (4)

14 Town served by the LNWR, GWR and Cambrian at a joint station built partly over the River Severn (10)

17 Fuel to which the Vale of Rheidol steam engines were converted (3)

18 Biggest of the 'Big Four' (1,1,1)

20 Stewart's, perhaps (4)

23 —— Park would have been the Princess of Wales's local station had it not been closed a year before she was born! (7)

24 Ends of the line! (7)

25 SE&CR station and tunnel between Faversham and Canterbury (7)

27 Loch ——, waterway alongside which the West Highland line runs and which gives its name to GNR 'K2' No 61782 and more recently 37027 (3)

30 North Staffordshire Railway headquarters (5)

31 The 'u' of dmu (4)

34 River crossed by the famous viaduct at Balcombe on the Brighton line (4)

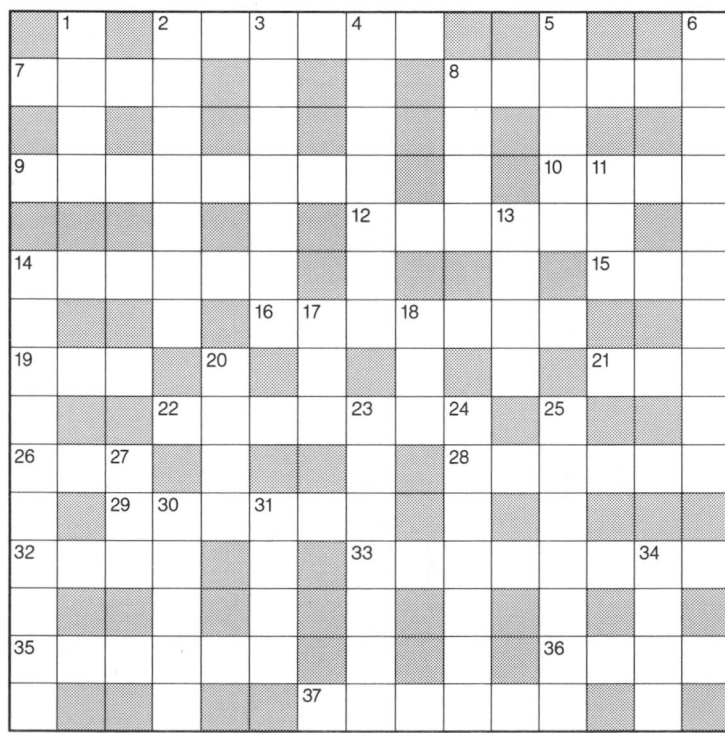

WHAT'S IN A NAME?

. . . or what name's in it? Here are some blank-looking nameplates
— can you name the steam or diesel class each belonged to?

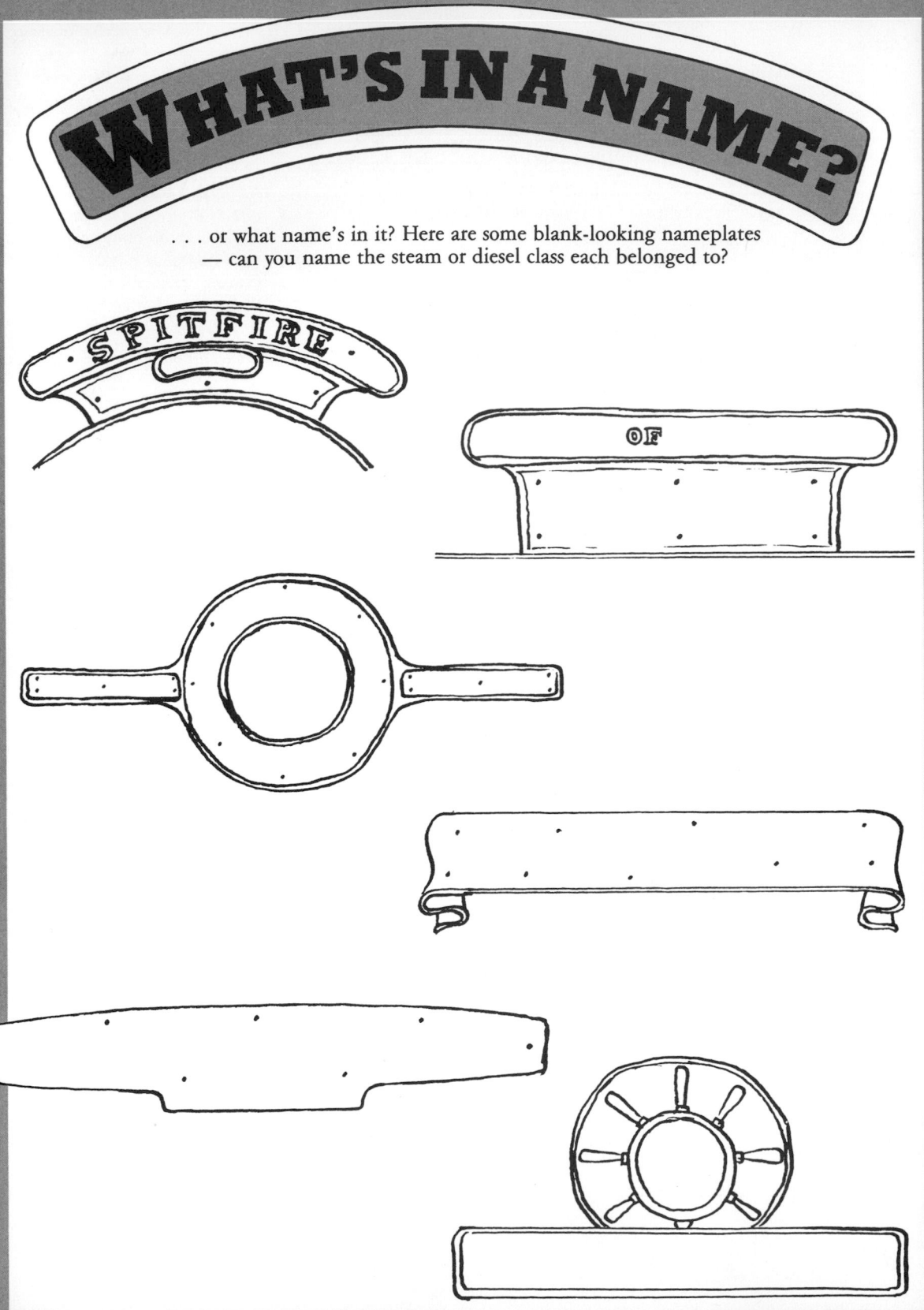

Solve the 'named train' clues below and enter the answers in the boxes. The shaded squares will then spell out the name of a famous train, and the two sets of numbered squares, on the left and right, taken in order, will spell out the down train's two principal destinations.

HEADBOARDS

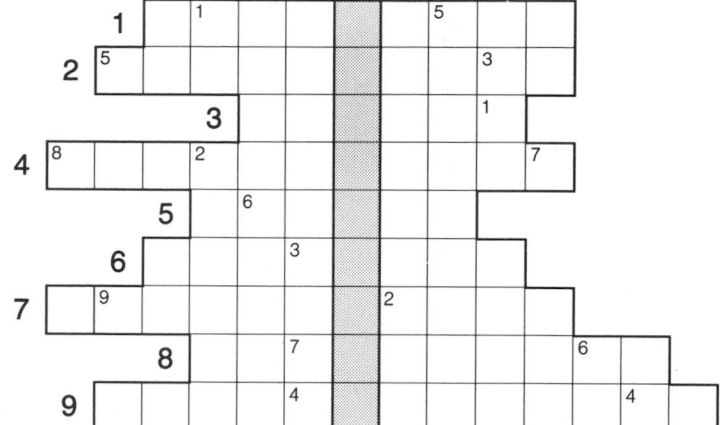

Clues

1 Paddington-Carmarthen express (3,6)

2 Express travelling the length of the original Great Western line, introduced to mark the centenary in 1935 (10)

3 '—— Scotsman', London-Edinburgh express introduced in 1928 (6)

4 Name given in 1929 to the Pullman train between London and Paris (6,5)

5 'Master' craftsman running between Marylebone and Sheffield (6)

6 King's Cross-Edinburgh express instituted in 1956 (8)

7 Rivers linked by a Midland line express running via the Settle & Carlisle line (6-5)

8 LNER streamliner introduced in 1937 to mark an important event of that year (10)

9 Shoreline which formed the destination of the West Country express from Waterloo, named in 1925 (8,5)

1 Why is a signalman referred to as a 'bobby'?

2 Why were the level crossing gates at Newcastleton on the Waverley route padlocked against an up sleeper train by local residents on 5 January 1969?

3 Why did up trains pass in opposite directions at Exeter St Davids?

4 Why is there no place called Verney, when there is a Verney Junction station on the Metropolitan and LNW railways?

5 Why did the GWR bolt two gas turbine aero engines and a 325-gallon tanker of jet fuel to a 'conflat' wagon for experiments at Dowlais Top in 1947?

6 Why was SR 'Schools' Class No 923 *Uppingham* renamed *Bradfield*?

7 Why was Bopeep Junction, Hastings, so named?

8 Why was the GWR's 'six foot' actually nearer 10'6"?

9 Why was the LNWR's new railway junction at Coppenhall called Crewe?

10 Why was the M&GNJR not absorbed into the LNER group until 1936?

11 Why was Waterloo station so named?

12 Why was the location of the headquarters of the Cambrian Railways, Wales's largest independent system, unusual?

PICTURE THE SCENE

KING'S CROSS APPROACHES

In early 1977 the first few gantries for electrification were appearing outside King's Cross, but apart from the lack of semaphore signalling, the scene was little changed from steam days.

1 What is the name of the tunnels in the background, leading down to the terminus?

2 What is the name of the tunnels on top of which the photograph was taken?

3 What feature crossing the line above the tunnels just outside King's Cross station necessitated the severe dip down to the terminus?

4 In mechanical signalling days, there was a signal box between the slow and fast lines just beyond the left-hand pier of the overbridge. What was its name?

5 Which pre-Grouping suburban company built the line which crosses over the GNR on the viaduct?

6 On 1 May 1968, a 'Deltic' and No 4472 *Flying Scotsman* were photographed and filmed leaving King's Cross simultaneously. What event was being marked?

7 In which year were HSTs introduced on to East Coast Main Line services?

8 Where is the next present-day power box to the north on the East Coast Main Line operating with King's Cross?

9 What station marked the initial northern limit of electrification on the King's Cross suburban route, where a change of trains was necessary?

WEST COAST, EAST COAST

Rivalry between the principal routes to Scotland, those taking the west and east coasts, engendered some famous moments in British railway history, and this puzzle gives you the opportunity to run up and down both routes! Solve the numbered groups of clues and write the answers in the 'up' and 'down' lines of the grid (the 'down' answers will read upwards and the up ones downwards!). The last letter of each answer in a group is the first letter of the next. When the answers are all in place, the names of London stations will appear in the lower box, Scottish destinations in the upper box, and places passed *en route* in the intermediate boxes, West Coast Main Line on the left, East Coast Main Line on the right.

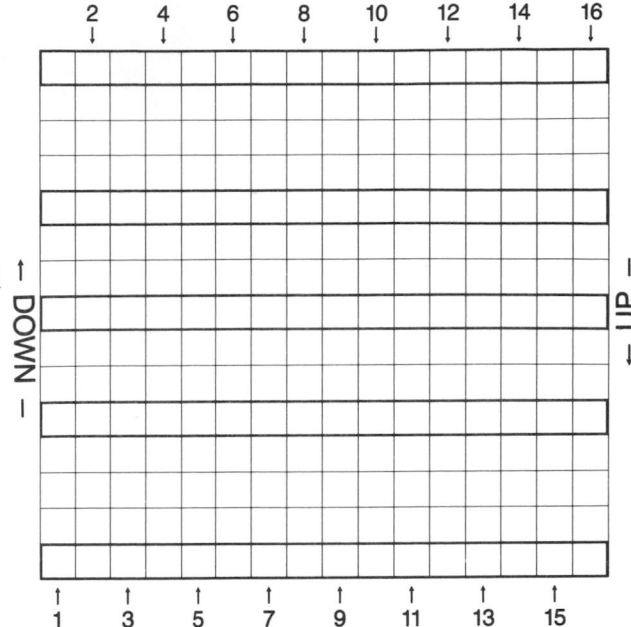

Up lines

2 Site of the next bridge over the river after the Forth Bridge (5); ill-fated tilting train (1,1,1); junction complex between Derby and Nottingham (5); GWR station between Bridgend and Maestag (5)

4 There are only six miles in the 100 between Craigendoran and Fort William at this gradient! (5); LSWR station near Petersfield (4); '—— and ticket' single line working (5); —— Augustus (4)

6 *Lord of the* ——, GWR engine shown at the 1851 Great Exhibition (5); group of coaches kept marshalled together (3); Yarmouth South —— (4); —— Fitzwarren, GWR smash of 1940 (6)

8 —— Bridge & Broseley (BWR) (4); —— Hill, Leeds shed (7); Glasgow Eastfield TMD depot code (2); Settle & Carlisle station (4); Tinsley TMD depot code (2)

10 Taff —— Railway (4); —— Green for Crowland (M&GNJR) (3); —— Valley Junction, south of Penrith (4); —— Eastern Railway (5); Sir Nigel Gresley's initials (1,1,1)

12 Secondary running line (6); principal running line (4); —— -y-Bwlch (Festiniog Railway) (3); complex served by Birmingham International station (1,1,1); line jointly controlled by the GCR, GNR and Midland Railway (1,1,1)

14 —— Junction, Newport (GWR) (4); Newton-le- —— (LNWR) (7); colloquial term for a detonator (4); Royal Mail railway vehicle (1,1,1)

16 Locomotive's adhesion aid (4); river unsuccessfully bridged by Stephenson at Chester (3); *River* ——, R&ER 15-inch gauge 2-8-2 of 1923 (3); LB&SCR junction for the Brighton and Lewes lines (6); initially, the author who said 'To travel hopefully is a better thing than to arrive' (1,1,1)

Down lines

1 Collectively, Nos 5043-5063 (5); detach a coach from a moving train (4); —— Main (NER) (5); NER 43-arch viaduct over the Tees near Stockton (4)

3 Location of the Royal Albert Bridge (7); —— Bank, LNWR junction for Morecambe (4); '—— Centre', the modern booking office! (6)

5 Term for a signal in the clear position (3); former county between the Forth and Tay Bridges (4); additional train (5); *Steady* —— (3); line between Manchester and Altrincham (1,1,1,1)

7 Device securing a rail in a chair (3); NRM home (4); town on the Windermere branch from Oxenholme (6); HR station just short of the summit between Dingwall and The Mound (5)

9 Newton Heath TMD depot code (2); Healey Mills TMD depot code (2); 2-6-0 wheel arrangement (5); extent of track under the supervision of a PW gang (6); warning sound in the GWR's ATC (4)

11 NER east coast town and Colliery stations (6); railway based at Derby (7); —— Holes Tunnel (4)

13 BR's express parcels service (3,4); SE&CR junction for Camber (3); Great —— Railway (7)

15 GCR General Manager, 1902-22 (3,3); area of goods sidings (4); Great Western Society HQ (6); Tyseley TMD depot code (2)

Across

1 Park on the Bluebell (9)

5 Colossal lattice iron viaduct on the NER cross-Pennine line near Kirkby Stephen (5)

7 Makers of the engines used in the 'Deltics' (6)

8 Terminus of a tramway from Quainton Road on the Met&GC (5)

10 and 5 down —— and ——, quaintly named SE&CR station at Sevenoaks (3 and 4)

11 and 9 down Lists of numbers indicating the sequence of pulling operations in a mechanical signal box (5,5)

13 Brunel's famous one at Maidenhead was the 'flattest' brick one in the world (4)

15 Port linked with Chester by a railway opened in 1848 (8)

17 Port linked with Callendar by a railway fully opened in 1880 (4)

18 Distance between supports of a bridge (4)

21 Naval hero commemorated by 'Jubilee' No 45659 (5)

22 BR refreshment rooms wares which are still the butt of ill-informed, ill-deserved 'humour'! (4)

25 Mechanism operating a steam locomotive's valves, for instance (4)

26 *Tudor* —— (No 60528) (8)

29 Northern terminus of the Isle of Wight Railway (4)

30 —— Hall, penultimate station on the GER's Ongar branch (5)

32 Initials of the organization that replaced the Railway Executive in 1962 (1,1,1)

33 *Golden* ——, 'A4' No 60023 (5)

34 Essential items of equipment in guards' vans and platelayers' huts! (6)

36 Gradient for 22 of the 28 miles between Cambridge Chesterton Junction and Brandon on the Thetford line! (5)

37 Railway ticket pioneer (9)

Down

1 *Doctor* ——, 'Canadian' 'Pacific' No 10 of the RH&DR (3)

2 Station between Pier Head and St Johns Road in 29 across (9)

3 —— *Line CGT*, 'Merchant Navy' No 35019 (6)

4 —— Valley Railway, preserved line (4)

5 See 10 across

6 Canadian province after which 'Jubilee' No 45562 was named (7)

8 '—— Scots', original nickname of what became the LMS 'Patriots' (4)

9 See 11 across

12 Device fitted to steam locomotives (and some diesels) to enable them to use water troughs (5)

14 Locomotive Superintendant of the GER, 1885-1907 (6)

16 Name of the first (numerically) 'West Country' 'Pacific' (6)

19 Rescues a locomotive or line for posterity (9)

20 'A1' 'Pacifics' —— *British* (No 60161) or —— *Eastern* (No 60147) (5)

23 Severe gradient (7)

24 Part of the exhaust that should not be seen on a well-fired steam locomotive! (5)

27 Weight of the vehicles of a train without passengers or luggage (4)

28 Northern terminus of a former narrow gauge Devon line (6)

31 On the GWR, he may have been of Eldon, Mount Edgcumbe or St Germans (4)

32 Colour of Caledonian Railway locomotives (4)

35 'A2/3' 'Pacifics' —— *Castle* (No 60523) or —— *Chariot* (No 60527) (3)

CENTRAL LINE

Fill in the blanks in the names of the London Underground stations listed below (all five-letter words), enter the answers in the grid, reading downwards, and an appropriate word will appear in the central row of boxes.

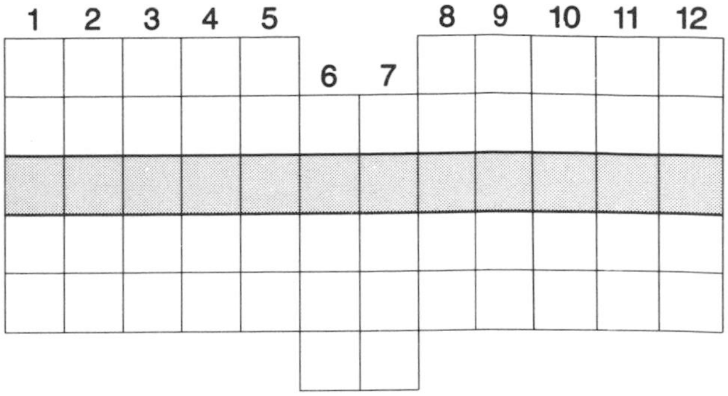

Clues

1 St —— 's Park
2 —— Park (Victoria/Piccadilly)
3 —— End
4 ——fields
5 New ——
6 —— Park (Metropolitan/District)
7 Surrey ——
8 ——dale
9 —— City
10 West, East or North ——
11 —— Farm
12 Ruislip ——

PANTOGRAPHS

Enter the answers to the clues into these 'pantograph' shapes. Each answer is a five-letter word from the name of one of the Class '86s' or '87s', and is entered from the numbered square in the direction stated. The letters at the 'corners' of the 'pantographs' are shared by two or more words.

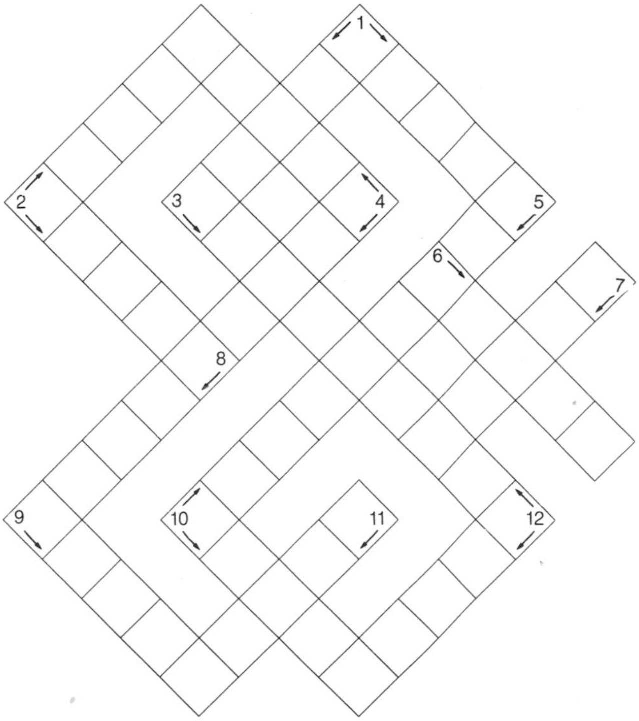

Clues

1 down left   *The —— Tabler*
1 down right   *—— Sovereign*
2 up   *—— of Fife*
2 down   *The ——*
3 down   *Abraham ——*
4 up   *Robert the ——*
4 down   *Robert ——*
5 down   *L.S. ——*
6 down   *Lancashire ——*
7 down   *—— Pan*
8 down   *City of —— on Trent*
9 down   *William Webb ——*
10 up   *Sir —— Johnson*
10 down   *Sir Charles ——*
11 down   *Lord of the ——*
12 up   *—— Neave*
12 down   *—— Chapelon*

SIGN ON

What are the meanings of these lineside signs?

1

2

3

4

5

6

7

8

What is the missing figure?

TEN YEARS ON

A lot of space has been devoted so far to seeing how much we know about railway history, some of it right back to the early days, but how much can you remember of the events of 1979 — just ten years ago?

1   *January*: ASLEF members undertook a series of 24-hour strikes. Who was the general secretary of ASLEF at that time?

2   *February*: Demolition of a cast-iron and glass roof at a station on the Midland main line was halted by the DoE until it could be decided whether or not it should be listed. Which station?

3   *March*: See the picture question

4   *King George V* was unable to return from Didcot later in the day. What was the problem?

5   What happened on the East Coast Main Line on 17 March which severely disrupted Anglo-Scottish services?

6   *April*: A head-on collision on Scottish region, despite a 'fail-safe' signalling system, claimed seven lives. Where did it take place?

7   *May*: A new 2¾-mile length of the London Underground was opened between Baker Street and Charing Cross — on which line?

8   The Great Rail Club for young travellers was launched. Its name was later changed — to what?

9   *June*: The Family Railcard was introduced. How much did the card cost?

Picture question: *March — King George V* storms westwards through the London suburbs near Old Oak Common. What was the special train commemorating?

10 *August*: The first accident involving an HST occurred when a train became entirely derailed at over 70 mph but remained upright. Where did it happen?

11 The replica of *Rocket* spent a week running up and down 250 yards of track in London prior to moving to York. Where was the track laid?

12 *September*: It was announced that part of the East Coast Main Line saw the world's fastest rail journey under 100 miles, at an average speed of 106.5 mph — between which two stations?

13 Traveller's Fare celebrated the centenary of railway catering. A special train toured the country — what was it called?

14 The first train with a dining car ran on 1 November 1879 — between which two cities?

15 *October*: An eminent statesman unveiled a Class '86/2' electric locomotive at Euston bearing his name. Who was he, and where, appropriately, did the train then depart for, carrying politicians and delegates?

16 Four accelerated HST services were introduced prior to the full timetable to start in May 1980 — on which route?

17 Two trains from Glasgow collided and toppled on to the shores of the Tay — near which station?

18 Sir Peter Parker, BRB Chairman, and 350 of his staff moved to new premises at Euston station. Where had they been accommodated until then?

19 *December*: The prototype APT reached a record speed on 12 December between Quintinshill and Lockerbie. What was the speed?

20 A particular type of rail commuter demonstrated outside BRB headquarters following a certain ban by BR on commuter trains from January 1980. What was the ban?

THE LONG AND THE TALL

Can you identify the locations of these three signal boxes?

LEVER LEADS II

See page 67 for how to solve this puzzle. In this example, the theme is railway junctions, and each of the four levers will 'set the route' for a well-known railway centre and junction, spelled out by the initial letters of the answers to the clues numbered below each, as before.

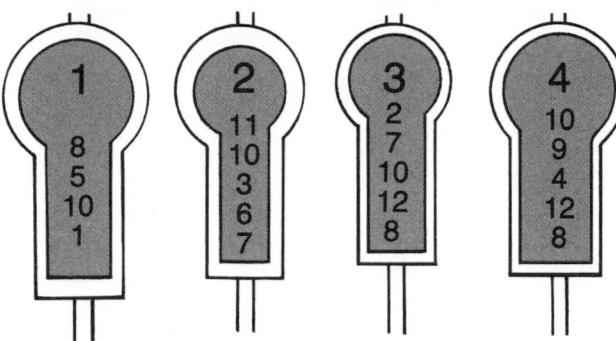

Clues

1 GWR junction for the Tetbury and Cirencester branches (6)

2 Triangular North London Railway junction north of Broad Street (7)

3 S&DJR junction of the Burnham and Bath lines (10)

4 'Far north' Highland junction of the Wick and Thurso lines (9)

5 GWR junction of the Ledbury and Chepstow lines just across the Severn from Gloucester (4)

6 Famous Hertfordshire junction station beyond which the North begins! (7)

7 Junction west of Newport (Mon), leading to the GWR line to the Vale of the same name (4)

8 Junction just beyond the extreme western end of the Nene Valley Railway (7)

9 Junction at the SW end of the Weston-super-Mare cut-off (6)

10 Colourful and picturesque name of the junction at the southern end of the M&SWJR near Andover (3,5)

11 GWR junction north of Exeter St Davids where the LSWR Devon and Cornwall lines diverge (6,6)

12 Nursery rhyme junction of the LB&SCR and SE&CR lines at Hastings (6)

COLLOQUIALLY SPEAKING

The following words or expressions are all colloquial or jargon railway terms. Do you know what they all mean?

1 To blow up

2 Board

3 Consolidation

4 The four-foot

5 The six-foot

6 Lanky

7 On the cushions

8 Peg

9 Hot box

10 Dod

Across

5 Familiar name for the concourse at Paddington (4)

8 Goods sector of BR (11)

9 Maintenance area between and beneath the rails in a depot (3)

10 Terminus of a short branch from Radley south of Oxford (8)

12 Liverpool —— Hill (4)

15 Semaphore signal controlling the entrance to the section ahead (7)

18 Place linked with Orston on the GNR in Notts — but not Watford, John! (5)

19 *William Webb* ——, Class '86' popular at Rugby? (5)

20 The 22 arches of the NER's Kirkstall Road viaduct are a prominent feature of this city (5)

21 Outer London SE&CR station on the line to Slades Green (5)

23 Power source of *Cyclopede*, perhaps the Rainhill Trials' most unusual 'locomotive' (5)

24 *Golden* bird of No 60023 (5)

26 LT&SR station on the Tilbury line, just across the Thames from 21 across (7)

28 Headquarters of the Isle of Wight Railway (4)

30 Grid forming the base of a steam locomotive's combustion chamber (4-4)

32 *River* ——, Ravenglass & Eskdale Railway locomotive, and the oldest 15-inch gauge locomotive in service anywhere (3)

33 —— Arms, the original 1844 terminus of the South Eastern and London & Croydon railways (11)

34 County served almost exclusively by the SE&CR (4)

Down

1 Animal used as the emblem of Toton TMD (6)

2 Class of Nos 72000-72009 (4)

3 '—— and wheel', early British Railways badge (4)

4 Third rail pick-up device on an electric locomotive or unit (4)

6 The 'a' of 'mas' (6)

7 City whose Victoria station was shared by the GCR and GNR (10)

11 Principal locomotive works of the NER (9)

13 What BR began to do following the Modernisation Plan of 1955 (9)

14 Sir Herbert ——, General Manager of the LSWR and first General Manager of the Southern Railway (6)

15 Locomotive which hauled the LNER's inaugural 'Silver Jubilee' train on 27 September 1935 (6,4)

16 Loch giving its name to a station on the Callendar and Oban line (3)

17 'Gone with ——', acronym of the GWR (6)

22 '—— Dien', motto of the Festiniog Railway (3)

25 Principal locomotive works of the GCR (6)

27 Name of 'EM2' electric locomotive No 27002 (6)

29 —— *Marischal*, 'A2/3' 'Pacific' No 60502 (4)

30 Front edge of a platform . . . (4)

31 . . . and the name given to terminal platforms in a through station (4)

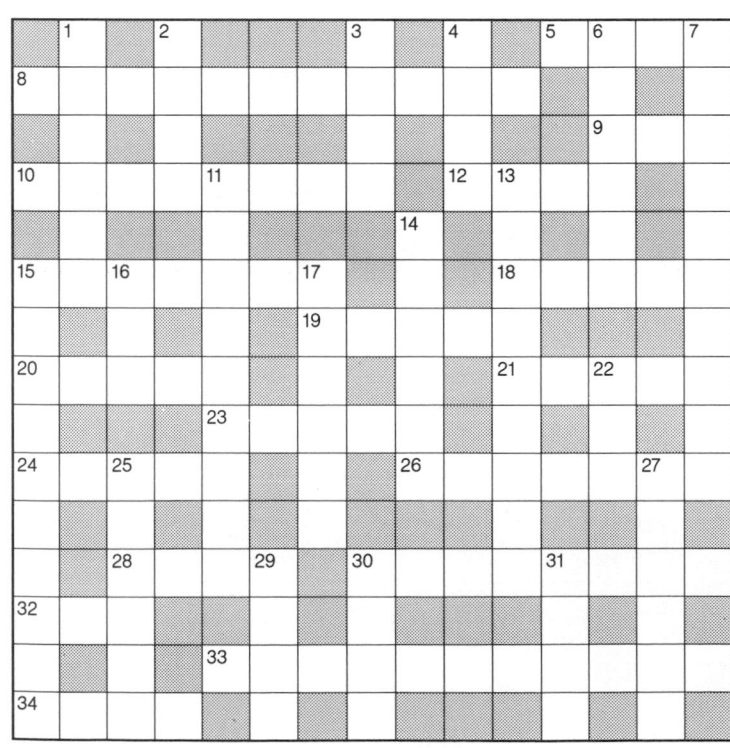

ARMS AND LIVERIES

This puzzle, based on the shape of the BR 'double arrow' emblem, deals with the liveries and, in many cases, very elegant coats of arms of the old railway companies. The across clues fit into the horizontal sections, while the down clues zig-zag downwards, interlocking with the acrosses at the intersections. The last letter of each answer is the first letter of the next word (where there is one).

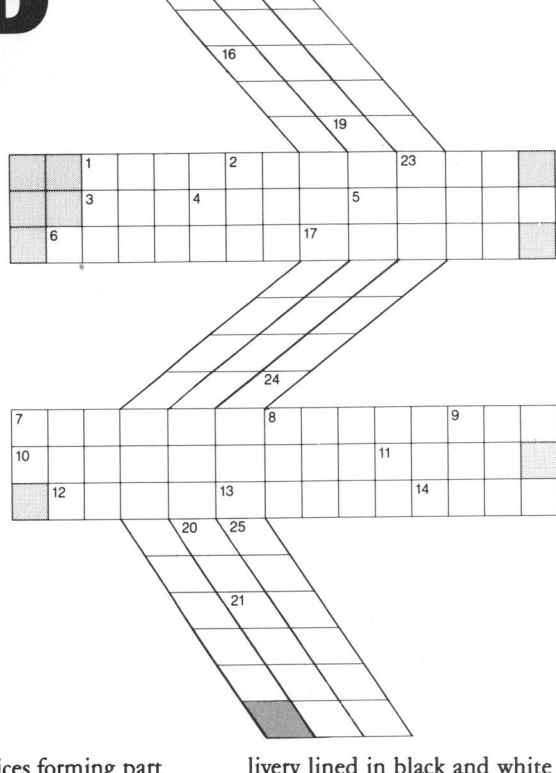

Across

1 'Chocolate and ——', famous GWR carriage livery (5)

2 '—— and child', principal component of the Furness Railway's arms (7)

3 Prominent part of the coat of arms of the railway referred to in 17 down, which gave it its nickname (4)

4 Type of red and white 21 down historically linking Lancashire and Yorkshire and appearing on many coats of arms to represent England (5)

5 Arms seen on TPOs (5)

6 Company whose motto, 'Forward', was adopted by the LNER after the Grouping (5,7)

7 City paired with 15 down on the arms of the GWR (7)

8 Name given to the painting applied on boiler bands, around tenders, cab-sides, carriage panelling etc (6)

9 Company whose elaborate emblem (prior to 1910) included the arms of London and Scotland and 12 towns, including, of course, 10 across (1,1,1)

10 Kent city, one of three whose arms were included in the emblem of the LC&DR (10)

11 Famous railway city whose coat of arms appears as part of the badges of the L&YR, GNR and NER (4)

12 Heraldic devices forming part of the arms of Leeds, as seen in the badges of the Midland and North Eastern railways (5)

13 Colour of Britain's first streamlined train (6)

14 '—— blue', BR's standard loco livery after 1965 (4,4)

Down

15 City arms combined with those of Barnsley on a crest bearing the date 1880 (4)

16 City whose arms appear with those of 6 across on the GWR, and are also featured in the emblems of many other railways (6)

17 Words on certain locomotive tanks or tenders flanking the railway arms which incorporated the emblem referred to in 3 across (5,8)

18 Winged heraldic creature prominent on the Midland Railway's coat of arms (6)

19 Railway whose locomotives carried a light or apple green livery lined in black and white (5,7)

20 Company whose emblem combined the coats of arms of 4 across and Berwick-upon-Tweed (1,1,1)

21 Emblem used to represent England on numerous railway coats of arms (4)

22 Eastern county city whose arms do not appear, surprisingly, in the GER and GNR emblems, but do appear, also surprisingly perhaps, in the Midland's badge (7)

23 Another Eastern county city whose arms do appear, not surprisingly, in the GER badge! (7)

24 Animal symbolising Kent in the arms of the SER and LC&DR (5)

25 Device surprisingly rarely seen on railway coats of arms, but prominent, and flanked by wings, on the top of 5 across's emblem (6)

THE BIG FOUR IV: SOUTHERN RAILWAY

1 What was unusual about the original valve gear of Bulleid's 'Merchant Navy' Class 'Pacifics'?

2 To whom was Bulleid assistant and on which railway before he moved to the Southern?

3 What term was used by Bulleid to describe the streamlining of his 'Pacifics'?

4 Which remarkable SR class was designed by Bulleid in 1942 to give maximum tractive effort with minimum axle weight?

5 Which Southern class of 4-4-0s was claimed to be the most powerful engine of that type in Europe?

6 In October 1946, *Channel Packet* hauled the inaugural post-war run of a famous titled train dating from 1929. Which one?

7 What was unusual about the exhaust beats of the 'Lord Nelson' Class as originally built?

8 Which was the last Pullman service to be put into operation by the Southern, in 1947?

9 In 1946, the Southern purchased 14 'switchers' from the USA. What are switchers?

10 In which year was the Brighton line electrified?

11 What was unique about the three five-car sets used for the electrified 'Brighton Belle'?

12 What aspect of the Southern's massive electrification and modernisation programme of the 1930s were dubbed unkindly 'Super Wireless Sets'?

13 What was unusual, in terms of subsequent Southern Railway standardisation, about the pre-Grouping electrification of the LB&SCR?

14 The Southern Railway was the first of the Big Four to establish a particular department, under the influence of its General Manager, Sir Herbert Walker. Which department?

15 Which famous narrow gauge line was closed by the Southern in 1935?

16 Why was non-stop running between Waterloo and Exeter impossible on the Southern Railway?

17 What type of locomotives were Nos 10201, 10202 and 10203, designed by the Southern but not completed until the 1950s?

18 How many different destinations were served by the coaches of the 'Atlantic Coast Express' in the 1920s?

19 What was significant about the Southern's early move to renumber the platforms at London's Victoria in 1925?

20 The last General Manager of the Southern Railway became the first Chairman of the nationalised Railway Executive in 1948, and had a 'Battle of Britain' 'Pacific' named after him. Who was he?

ADDITIONAL SERVICE

Add the number of platforms at Waterloo to *Mallard*'s record-breaking year. Then add the year the Forth Bridge opened, the number carried by the preserved *Blue Peter* and *Electra*'s class number. The result is a famous steam locomotive — which?

WATERLOO DEPARTURE

How quickly can you identify the following eight LSWR stations on this Waterloo 'departure board'?

1	W										
2	A										
3	T										
4	E										
5	R										
6	L										
7	O										
8	O										

Clues

1 Town linked to Bodmin by an ancient steam railway opened in 1834 (10)

2 Headquarters station of the Mid-Hants Railway, 'The Watercress Line' (9)

3 Somerset station on the main line, shared with the S&DJR (11)

4 Site, formerly known as Bishopstoke, of the main LSWR locomotive works (9)

5 LSWR Surrey station and junction, also the western end of the North London line (8)

6 Summit and tunnel on the Basingstoke-Weymouth line, near Micheldever (10)

7 —— St Mary, intermediate station on the Sidmouth/ Budleigh branch (6)

8 Station on the Plymouth line, just before Meldon Viaduct and Junction (10)

PULLMAN PREDICAMENT

Hidden in this 'Pullman car' are the names of 37 locomotive-hauled Pullmans plus, to give you a start, the name of the NRM's preserved Parlour Car 'Topaz' already located. The names may read backwards, forwards, up, down, or diagonally, always in a straight line but never skipping letters. All the letters are used at least once except the Xs, which are not used at all. See how quickly you can find them all.

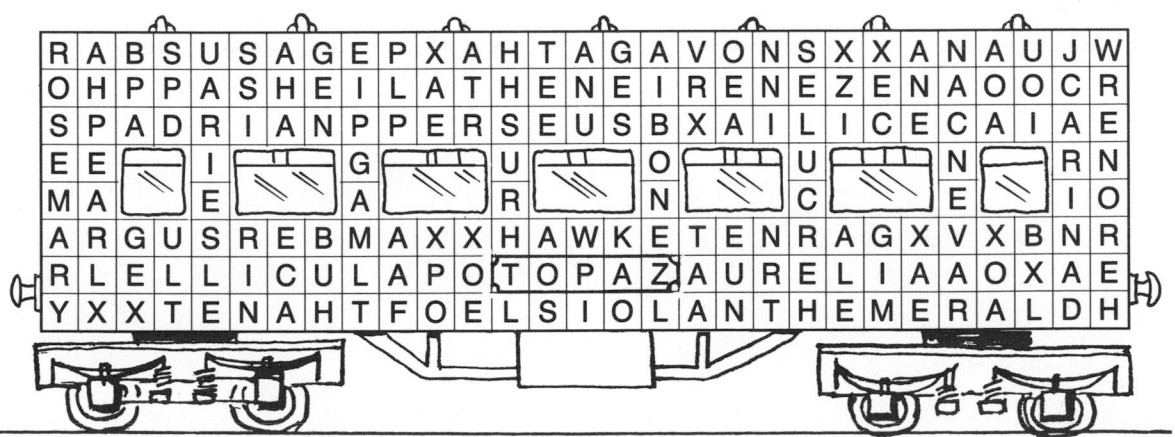

WYLAM

I photographed the remarkable elevated signal box at Wylam, on the Newcastle-Carlisle line, in September 1982.

1 The Newcastle & Carlisle Railway was the first main line to cross the country. When was it completed?

2 Which company assumed control of the N&C in 1862?

3 The famous pioneering steam locomotive *Wylam Dilly* was built in 1813 to operate the Wylam Colliery wagonway. Who was the locomotive's designer?

4 What is, or was, a 'dilly'?

5 The designer's more famous locomotive is preserved in the Science Museum in London. What is its name?

6 In pre-steam locomotive days, the Wylam wagonway's rails were made from what material?

7 A famous railway pioneer was born in a cottage alongside the wagonway in 1781. Who was he?

8 One of the contenders in the later Rainhill Locomotive Trials of 1829 was a foreman blacksmith at Wylam Colliery. Who was he?

9 Reverting to the photograph, the three-aspect signal is displaying 'Danger'. In which position would the 'Caution' aspect appear?

10 The diamond-shaped plate indicates that a train brought to a stand there is exempt from Rule 55. What basically does this rule require of a train crew?

EARLY SIGNALLING

This engraving which appeared in the *Illustrated London News* in September 1866 shows the 'AB Signalbox' of the South Eastern Railway at London Bridge.

1 What colour was used in the early days to indicate a 'Caution' aspect at night?

2 Which railway company used the 'disc and crossbar' type of semaphore signal?

3 What name is given to the pre-fixed-signal method of signalling where a sand-timer was often an essential piece of equipment?

4 Which railway line from the capital first adopted the semaphore signal, in 1841?

5 What was at the time the longest railway telegraph in Britain was installed by the LSWR between Nine Elms and which south coast port?

6 The equipment had been patented by Mr Cooke and his partner. What was his partner's name?

7 Which serious railway accident in 1876 spelled the end for the slotted post type of semaphore signal . . .?

8 . . . and what special type of semaphore signal was adopted by the GNR as a result?

9 Which safety device connected with signalling was recommended in the report of the Hawes Junction crash of 1910, and is now almost universal?

10 What important change was made to the appearance of distant signals in the 1870s?

Across

2 Large brake and signal manufacturing company (12)

7 Cover for a steam locomotive's regulator valve on top of the boiler (4)

8 Famous Railway Guide (1,1,1)

9 NBR station on the Waverley route, or GER station between Cambridge and King's Lynn (4)

10 Type of 'tail' possessed by the LNER's 'Coronation' observation car (6)

11 —— Green, first station on the M&GNJR out of Peterborough (3)

12 Highland/GN of SR station where the former joined the latter's line eastwards to Aberdeen (5)

13 —— Carlisle, NBR terminus on the Solway estuary (4)

15 Device whereby a distant signal on the same post as a home cannot be cleared unless the home is also 'off' (4)

17 'West Country' 'Pacific' No 34096, named after a village near Padstow (7)

18 —— Street Goods, Midland GN and GER depots outside Fenchurch Street (4)

20 —— *Aircraft Command*, 'Battle of Britain' No 34049 (4)

22 Those of the headquarters of the LMS were in Eversholt House at Euston (7)

24 Belle ——, signal box between the tunnels outside King's Cross (4)

26 God and planet giving their name to 'Jubilee' No 45698 (4)

29 G&SWR terminus of the line north from Ardrossan (5)

31 No 18000 was such a turbine (3)

32 *Channel* ——, No 35001 (6)

33 Name of the South Devon Railway broad gauge 0-4-0T put on display on Newton Abbot station (4)

34 First station on the Teign Valley line from Exeter — avoided by Julius Caesar? (6)

35 A famous railway one took place in 1888 (4)

36 Triangular junction for Bristol and Bath on the Midland line (12)

Down

1 Picturesquely named junction between the SE&CR and LB&SCR at Hastings (6)

2 LNWR junction for the Liverpool and Warrington main lines north of Crewe (6)

3 Code name for an engineers' ballast train brake van (5)

4 Lickey, perhaps (7)

5 Town linked to Wisbech by tramway (6)

6 Type of crank essential to the operation of a steam locomotive's valve gear (9)

9 Class of Maunsell 4-4-0s on the Southern Railway (7)

14 *King's* ——, 'Royal Scot' No 46161 (3)

15 Westgate, Birchington and Sheerness are all on it as well as on the SE&CR (3)

16 Deep-water dock built by the GCR and opened by King George V in 1912 (9)

17 Midland Railway junction south of Gloucester (7)

19 Thin end of the switch blade of a set of points (3)

21 Railway originally built to link Berwick and Edinburgh (1,1,1)

23 Queen St, General and Bute Road were all stations in this city (7)

25 'Stop, look and ——' (6)

27 *Bon* ——' 'A3' No 60154 (6)

28 —— House Road, unusually named station on the Severn & Wye Joint in the Forest of Dean (6)

30 LNWR Merseyside station and junction south of Liverpool (5)

END OF THE LINE

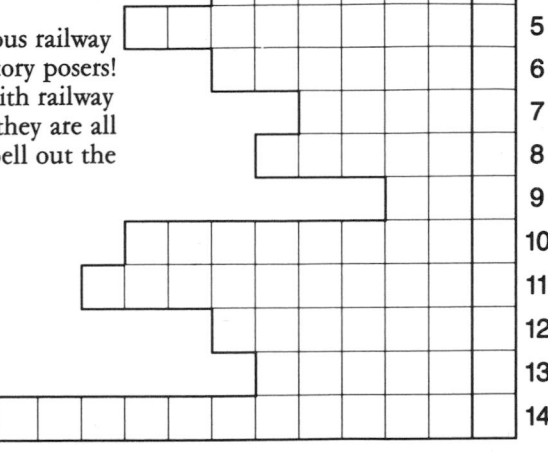

As we reach the end of our extremely long and arduous railway puzzle journey, here's a pair of appropriately valedictory posers!

In this one, answer the clues — they're all to do with railway termini — and enter the answers in the grid. When they are all in place, their last letters, reading downwards, will spell out the name of one of Britain's best-known termini.

Clues

1 Western terminus of the —— & Wigtownshire Joint Railway (11)

2 Terminus of a short LNWR branch from the main line at Cheddington . . . (9)

3 . . . and, 15 miles further north, of a branch from Wolverton (7,7)

4 LSWR seaside terminus of a branch from Worgret Junction (7)

5 North Wales seaside terminus at the end of a branch from a junction of the same name (9)

6 Northern seaside terminus of a GN of SR branch from Inveramsay (7)

7 Terminus of the long-defunct tramway from Quainton Road, Bucks (5)

8 Britain's northernmost terminus (6)

9 Railway whose Manchester terminus was Central (1,1,1)

10 Terminus of a GWR branch just east of Swindon (9)

11 East Coast terminus of a NER branch from Hull (10)

12 Identifying suffix applied to the Brighton terminus of the LB&SCR (7)

13 Resort at the end of a West Country GWR branch from St Erth (2,4)

14 Terminus of the Caledonian line to the Western Isles (12)

THE LAST WORD

And in rather a similar vein, a puzzle of 'lasts'. When you have answered all the clues, their first letters, taken in order, will spell out a term (6,4) which is an apt conclusion to this book.

Clues

1 The last such train ran on 20 May 1892 (5,5)

2 The last station on the Metropolitan branch via Ruislip (8)

3 The last of Brunel's timber viaducts was replaced on this GWR branch in Cornwall in 1934 (8)

4 The last CME of the Midland Railway (6)

5 The last steam locomotive built for British Railways (7,4)

6 The last CME of the North Eastern Railway (5)

7 The last railway works to build a steam locomotive for British Railways (7)

8 The last thing a signalman looks for to ensure a train is complete (4,4)

9 The last vehicle of the LNER's 'Coronation' during the summer months (11,3)

10 The last station on the 'Cornish Riviera's' journey (8)

Crossword No 1

Across: 1 Riddles 5 Gauge 10 Ivatt 11 Flyer 12 Tudor 13 Hunslet 14 Earls 15 Rod 17 Leek 19 Gnu 20 Schools 24 Six 25 Star 26 Wem 29 Bobby 30 Eastern 32 *Venus* 33 Three 34 Thame 35 Phone 36 'Yankees'

Down: 1 Rainhill 2 ('The) Drain' 3 Little 4 Scottish 6 *Alfred (the Great*) 7 Guy Granet 8 *Elder* 9 Arms 16 Oil 18 Edinburgh 21 CME 22 Oswestry 23 *Princess* 26 Wyvern 27 Manor 28 Ashton 29 Bath 31 Edale

Western Enterprise

					P	A	T	H	F	I	N	D	E	R		
R	E	L	I	A	N	C	E		U		U			M		
L		X			P	R	I	N	C	E	K			O		
E	M	P	E	R	O	R		B		T		Y	E	O	M	A	N
G		L			C		D	U	C	H	E	S	S		T		O
I	O		C			L	E		M		P	R	E	F	E	C	T
O		R	A	A	W	R	A		R	A					O		O
N		E	V		D	R	A	G	O	O	N		L	A	N	C	E	R
N	R	A	V	R		L			E			E		
A		O	L	D	O	A	K	C	O	M	M	O	N		N		
I		I		C		O		R		S	U	L	T	A	N	
R	I	F	L	E	M	A	N	N	C	D	E		N		U		
E		R		T		S	H		N		D	R	U	I	D	
F		N	E	W	T	O	N	A	B	B	O	T		I		O
K	I	N	G	O		R		L	U	I		O		O		M
R		B	R	I	S	T	O	L		C	A	N	T	O	N		I
E	R	L	N		E		C	E		A		U		R		N
B	A		E	N	V	O	Y	N	A	L		U		I		I
R	N	M	A		G		N		O
V	A	N	G	U	A	R	D		R	E	G	E	N	T		Q	U	E	E	N
N	E		N		E		R		E		R
D	R				R	E	N	O	W	N

Picture the Scene: Exeter St Davids

1 Hydraulic 2 December 1961 3 'Main' (line) 4 'Shunt ahead' or 'Calling on', allowing a train to proceed as far as the next signal prior to reversing back into the station 5 1 in 36 6 Exeter West 7 Exeter Queen Street 8 Totnes 9 Exeter St Thomas 10 7'0"

Gantry

Across: 3 Token 5 Crewe 7 Panel 8 Tyer 9 Frame 11 Disc 12 Lock 13 Home 14 Red 15 Sand drag 17 Distant 18 Block system 20 Fitter 21 Train describers 22 Route 23 ATC 25 GWR 26 AWS 27 Off 29 IBS (Intermediate block signals) 30 Derby 31 Rugby

Down: 1 Intermediate 2 Searchlight 4 Block instruments 6 Semaphore 10 Mechanical 16 Detector 19 York 24 Starting 25 Ground 28 Four

Crossword No 2

Across: 1 Brush 6 Racehorse 8 Napier 10 Retford 11 Edge Hill 12 *Albion* 16 Peg 18 Granite 19 Consett 20 NER 22 Smoker 27 Parkside 28 Tubular 30 Copper 31 Inverness 32 Stoke

Down: 1 Banker 2 St Ives 3 Fairlie 4 Bertha 5 Bo-Bo 7 Sidmouth 9 Rail 13 Link 14 Crampton 15 Lime 16 Pen 17 GCR 21 Express 23 Relent (*Relentless*) 24 Eric 25 Ashpit 26 George 29 Blea

Pointwork

1 Oakham 2 Kings Sutton 3 Sutton Bridge 4 Uttoxeter 5 Tonbridge 6 Nottingham 7 Leyton

8 Laira 9 Ramsgate 10 Exeter 11 Exmouth 12 Ribble, Ripley, Retford 13 Leek 14 Elstree 15 Tring 16 Greenford 17 Enfield 18 Durham 19 Monsal 20 Aber 21 Barnstaple, Barnt Green 22 Darlington 23 Lincoln

Titled trains

1 Fishguard 2 Heysham 3 Aberdeen 4 Aberystwyth 5 The 'Bristol Pullman' 6 The 'Brighton Belle' 7 The 'Manchester Pullman' 8 The 'Cornishman' 9 The 'Devon Belle' 10 The 'Elizabethan' 11 10 am 12 The 'Master Cutler' 13 The 'Golden Arrow' 14 The 'Hull Executive' 15 The 'Royal Scot' 16 Manchester London Road 17 'Limited' 18 The 'Silver Jubilee' in 1935 19 The 'Sunny South Express' 20 The 'Waverley'

On a plate

Coronation; *Highland Light Infantry, The City of Glasgow Regiment*; *Patriot*; GCR; *Tommy*, Class '76' No 26000; A running fox ('D49' 'Hunt' Class); A half football ('B17' Class); *Union of South Africa*, No 60009; D0280 *Falcon*, Brush

Works team

	C	H	U	R	C	H	W	A	R	D						
					H				R				A		
		P	U	R	I	E			F	A	I	R	B	U	R	N
		O			T		S		V				C		
P		L		B	E	A	T	T	I	E			H		
K	I	R	T	L	E	Y		L	R		N		W	E	B	B
C		I		E		O		P	H			U		
K		T		G	U	A		E	F	T		B		
E	A	S	T	L	E	I	G	H	D	E	R	B	Y	G	O	R	T	O	N
R		T			L	K		W	W			U		
S	W	I	N	D	O	N	C	R	E	W	E	C	O	W	L	A	I	R	S
G		R			Y		R	O	E			V		T
B	I	L	L	I	N	T	O	N		B		D	R		R		A
L		I		B			U				A		T		N
L	N		A	S	P	I	N	A	L	L		H		D		I
R		M		R		A		L		O		E		E		E
E		A		K				I		L		A		R
I		R				D	R	U	M	M	O	N	D	
A	D	A	M	S					E					
			H	U	R	R	Y	R	I	C	H	E	S		

Crossword No 3

Across: 4 Aber 9 Welland 10 Olive 11 Cary 12 Great (railway company names) 13 Steam 14 Ticket 16 Blue 17 *Owain* 18 London 25 Edward 26 Soham 27 Vine 28 *Planet* 30 Diner 31 Inner 32 East 33 Leeds 34 *Novelty* 35 Sand

Down: 1 Keighley 2 Bluebell 3 Knott End 5 Black ('Black Fives') 6 Royston 7 Fireman 8 Termini 15 Croydon 19 Cast-iron 20 Advanced 21 Concrete 22 Eskdale 23 Shunter 24 Empress 29 *Anson*

Arrivals and departures

Up: 1 Disc 2 Cromer 3 Rayner's 4 Shrub 5 Raynes 6 Silver 7 Ramp 8 Pwllheli 9 Cross 10 Shap 11 Pilning 12 Shed 13 Dray 14 Yarmouth 15 Drag 16 Grosmont

Down: 17 Leeds 18 Tail 19 Depot 20 Yard 21 *Gard* 22 *Neil* 23 Darlington 23A Oxford (Worcester and Wolverhampton) 24 Harlington 24A Neath

London's termini

1 Waterloo; the First World War 2 Euston (The 'Victoria' and the 'Euston') 3 King's Cross 4 Liverpool Street (the intensive pre-electrification suburban service of commuter trains, introduced in 1920) 5 London Bridge

6 LB&SCR 7 Beer barrel 8 Broad Street 9 LMS 10 St Pancras and King's Cross (respectively) 11 4 12 Charing Cross 13 Waterloo 14 King's Cross 15 A replica of one of a series of thirteenth-century crosses erected to mark the course of the funeral procession of Queen Eleanor from Lincoln to London. The original stood in Whitehall 16 Paddington 17 Victoria 18 The proposed demolition of the 'Euston Arch' 19 Great Western Railway 20 The London & Birmingham Railway, Euston **Picture question:** Cannon Street

Rush-hour rhyme

Across: 12 March 13 Peg 14 *Tetrarch* 16 Torpedo 21 Nine 23 *Whitelaw* 25 Robert 28 Hotel 35 Doncaster 37 Havant 41 Third 42 Brake
Down: 1 *Commonwealth* 2 *Merlin* 3 (*King*) *Uther* 4 *Eland* 5 Night 6 Witham 7 Oxted 8 'Prairie' 9 HST 10 *Sir Richard* 11 *Eton* 13 Panel 15 *Comet* 17 Electric 18 Gill 19 Newent 20 Irish 22 Old 24 Euston 26 Bude 27 Road 29 *Welsh* 30 Kentish 31 *Laird* 32 *Accord* 33 *Aden* 34 *Green* 36 Drag 38 APT 39 Tie 40 *Ark* 41 Two

'Commuter — one who spends his life
In riding to and from his wife;
A man who shaves and takes a train
And then rides back to shave again.'

E. B. White

The Big Four 1: LMS

1 George Stephenson 2 President of the Executive 3 10 am 4 The 'Corridor' 5 George Hughes 6 'Turbomotive' 7 10000 and 10001 8 Toton 9 It was the only stretch of level line between Huddersfield and Manchester 10 Hull & Barnsley 11 A single-decker motor-bus with interchangeable road and rail wheels 12 Mid-blue and silver 13 114 mph 14 *Fury* 15 Garrett articulated 2-6-6-2s 16 Bath (Green Park Station, formerly MR) 17 No 6200, *The Princess Royal* 18 Chicago

Blessed stations!

Bedford St Johns, Bristol St Philips, Cheltenham St James, Exeter St Davids, Exeter St Thomas, Glasgow St Enoch, London St Pancras, Southport St Lukes

Cardiff and St Marys were the 'red herrings'

Picture the scene: St Pancras

1 Via Leicester, Hitchin and the GNR to King's Cross 2 2nd class — all trains carried 1st and 3rd only 3 Thomas Hardy 4 10,000 5 West Hampstead 6 Water tower 7 Beer barrels from Burton 8 D99 9 British Transport Hotels 10 The British Library

Getting the road

Birmingham New St, Bradford Forster Sq, Cheltenham Malvern Rd, Derby Friargate, Exeter Queen St, Liverpool Lime St, Manchester London Rd, Northampton Bridge St, Nottingham Arkwright St, Plymouth North Rd, Worcester Foregate St

Leeds and Midland Rd were the 'red herrings'

Glasgow and Edinburgh

1 Bridge Street 2 They matched the piers of the old adjacent road bridge to aid navigation 3 St Pancras (Midland Railway) 4 963 5 The final stage of the London-Glasgow electrification 6 Cable 7 The 'blue trains' 8 13 9 A World War I collecting box, and popular rendezvous for Glaswegians 10 Queen Street 11 A locomotive — the Cowlairs incline was cable operated 12 Glasgow Queen Street 13 Almond Viaduct, Ratho

14 Haymarket 15 London's Waterloo 16 The restriction was imposed by the Bank of Scotland under the law of servitude and 'ancient lights' 17 North Bridge 18 Queen Street 19 Lothian Road 20 There was a locomotive (Class '27') at both ends

Scottish throats

Aberdeen Joint (north end); Oban; Edinburgh Waverley (west end)

Crossword No 4

Across: 3 *Electra* 7 Wye 9 *Pinza* 10 Doncaster 11 Thistle 12 *Osprey* 15 Redhill 18 Ashlar 21 AWS 22 Denham 23 Tenders 25 Cuckoo 31 Cardiff 32 Llandudno 33 Ongar 34 *Yes* (*Tor*) 35 Rushton
Down: 1 Spotter 2 *India* 3 Eastleigh 4 *Elder* 5 Tank 6 Adams 7 Water 8 Early 13 EAR 14 Fast 16 Dee 17 Lamp 19 (*Butler*) *Henderson* 20 Axe 22 Dmu 24 Salford 25 'Caley' 26 Class 27 (Light Railway) Order 28 (George Gilbert) Scott 29 Kings 30 (Col Robert) Edis

Roundhouse '62

1 Nene Valley 2 Yeovil 3 Leicester 4 Ryde 5 Edge 6 Eastfield 7 Docks 8 Springs Branch 9 Hill 10 Liverpool 11 Low Moor 12 Road 13 Dinting 14 Green 15 Nine 16 Exeter 17 Rugby 18 Yoker 19 Reading 20 Gateshead 21 Dock 22 Kentish Town 23 North 24 Holbeck 25 King's Cross 26 Swansea 27 Alexandra Dock

Camden, Stoke, Derby, Oxley, Burton

Diesel Depot

1 *Tryfan* 2 Norfolk 3 *Odin* 4 *North Star* 5 *Thames* 6 *Scythia* 7 *Own* 8 *Nimbus* 9 *Spartan* 10 Neville 11 *Endeavour*

Toton, Laira

Pacific puzzle

1 *Missenden* 2 *Clan* 3 Gresley 4 *Vulcan* 5 *Peter* 6 *Iron Duke* 7 Whitelaw 8 *Great Bear* 9 *Blue* 10 Dickens 11 *Coronation* 12 Gloucester 13 *Dornoch* 14 City

Top link

1 —— Cross, on the London Underground 2 Wellington (Duke of, Bank, Station) 3 *County of Somerset*, *County of Dorset*, principal train of the S&DJR 4 Types of carriages (GCR, GWR, LB&SCR) 5 Tunnels on the Settle & Carlisle line 6 'Belle' — named trains 7 Black — 'Five', *Watch*, *Prince* 8 Stations in Dover 9 Gloucester — Company, city station, *Duke of* 10 Each has or had a Queen Street station 11 Each has or had a Central station 12 . . . South Western Railway 13 North — railway company names 14 *Rocket*'s Rainhill opponents 15 Severn prefixes each 16 Stations on the GWR

Picture link: the signal box now preserved at Butterley is Ais Gill from the familiar location on the Settle & Carlisle line

Cab conundrum

Boiler pressure gauge, damper, firehole door, large ejector, live steam injector, regulator, reversing gear, sander, small ejector, steam brake, vacuum brake, vacuum gauge, washout plug, water gauge, whistle

Crossword No 5

Across: 1 Patrick 6 Stirling 8 Lawn 10 Met(ropolitan) 11 Nine 12 Elms 13 Ree 15 Road 17 Masham 20 BTC (British Transport Commission) 22 (George)

Whale   23 One (No 1)   24 Annan   25 Ned (Edward)
27 *Silver*   29 Area   30 Raj   32 Iron   33 Earl   35 GWR
36 East   38 St Helens   39 (Thomas) Brassey
Down: 1 PUL   2 Town   3 *Camelot*   4 Crosshead
5 Pier   6 Steam   7 Glenfinnan   9 Nidd   14 Crewe
Works   16 (William) Adams   18 *Aden*   19 Manor
20 Belle Isle   21 Code   26 *Emperor*   28 Rings   29 Aire
31 (*King*) John   34 Laps   37 Tay

Call to arms
LNWR: Britannia with her shield seated on a lion
LMS: The thistle of Scotland
GCR: Front view of a steam locomotive
FR: Prince of Wales feathers

Monarchs of the road
1 King's Cross   2 Slough and London   3 I. K. Brunel
4 Newcastle (Central)   5 Edward (eight times)   6 George
VI (6028)   7 Boadicea (70036)   8 Caledonian   9 Exeter,
Cardiff, Glasgow   10 GWR   11 George V   12 Elizabeth
II ('The Elizabethan')   13 *Princess Anne* (46202)
14 Tamar   15 Sandringham   16 'Queen of Scots'
17 1927   18 Carlisle   19 Paddington   **Picture question:**
Robert Stephenson (Royal Border Bridge, Berwick)

Picture the scene: Windsor & Eton
1 Windsor & Eton Riverside (LSWR)   2 Eton College
3 Central   4 Queen Victoria's Diamond Jubilee
5 Slough   6 London and Bristol   7 George VI, in 1936
8 Madame Tussauds   9 *The Queen* (No 3041)   10 River
Thames

The preservation scene I
1 The Tallylyn Railway, Wales   2 Dr Richard Beeching
3 The Great Western Society, Didcot   4 The Bluebell
Railway   5 Torbay & Dartmouth Railway   6 East Somerset
Railway   7 The 'Watercress Line' (Mid-Hants Railway)
8 Bressingham, Norfolk   9 Nene Valley Railway
10 Victoria Bridge   11 Great Central Railway London
Extension in the Loughborough area   12 Tyseley,
Birmingham   13 Sand   14 The original route was
submerged by a hydro-electric scheme reservoir   15 1′11½″
16 The River Gwili along whose valley it runs
17 Windermere   18 Settle & Carlisle (Selside)   19 Derby
Road, Southport   20 2-4-0T   **Picture question:** The Kent
& East Sussex Railway

Steam lines
Torbay & Dartmouth Railway, Kingswear; Severn Valley
Railway, Bewdley; North Yorks Moors Railway, near
Grosmont; North Norfolk Railway, Weybourne

Crossword No 6
Across: 1 TOPS (Total Operations Processing System)
4 *Isles*   7 LSWR   9 George   10 Hudson   12 Pea (the
Acme Thunderer is a railway whistle)   13 Fratton
15 Upwey   18 ECS (empty coaching stock)   19 Ely
20 ROD (Railway Operating Department)   21 Bay
22 *Trigo*   23 Angle   25 Ash   26 *Ark*   27 APT   28 Lap
29 Edale   30 Prosser   34 MSL (Manchester, Sheffield &
Lincolnshire)   35 *Wullie*   37 Edward   38 Kyle
39 Stays   40 'King'
Down: 2 Ongar   3 Scout   5 *Stepney*   6 Exhaust
7 LMS   8 *Wynd*   11 Dawlish   14 Aldgate   16 Yeomans
17 Hymek   20 *Royal*   21 Bagnall   24 Element
25 Appleby   31 'Shark'   32 End-on   33 Away   36 Lee

Marshalling
4, 9, 7, 1, 10, 8, 5, 3, 6, 2

Brass, Iron Duke, Royal Scot, Irish Mail, Black Five, four
foot, hand lamp, light engine, driving wheels, roundhouse, shed

Initial reaction
1 London, Tilbury & Southend Railway   2 Stratford-on-
Avon & Midland Junction Railway   3 British Transport
Commission   4 Manchester, Sheffield & Lincolnshire
Railway   5 West London Extension Railway   6 British
Railways Universal Trolley (for parcels)   7 Carriage &
Wagon (Department)   8 Empty Coaching Stock
9 Multiple aspect signalling   10 Continuous welded rail

Where's the station?
1 Dent   2 York   3 Honiton   4 Swindon   5 Didcot
6 Derby   7 Euston   8 Dover   9 Preston   10 Hitchin

Here and there
Goring & Streatley, Craven Arms & Stokesay, Glendon &
Rushton, Hawes Junction & Garsdale, Hayes & Harlington,
Basford & Bulwell, Knowle & Dorridge, Glastonbury &
Street, Chalfont & Latimer, Belgrave & Birstall

Three into one
1 Westbury   2 Dingwall   3 Clapham

Wisbech and Upwell Tramway

Empty stock I
Across: 1 Lodge   4 Wigan   7 *Mungo*   8 Acton
10 Chief   13 Dava   14 Lane   15 Rugby   33 Stamp
23 Loose   24 *Elder*   25 Esher
Down: 1 Lime   2 Dent   3 Enoch   4 Whale   5 Gate
6 Nene   9 Gas   10 Car   11 Fly   12 End   16 Upper
17 Belle   18 Isle   19 Sand   20 Loch   21 *Bear*

Slip coaches I
1 Twyford   2 Ahrons   3 Exmouth   4 Belfast   5 *Book
Law*   6 'Royal Scot'   7 *Kolhapur*   8 'Bristolian'
9 Festiniog   10 Barnstaple   11 Rotherwas   12 Motorail
13 *Kay*   14 Stirling   15 Tubular   16 Shropshire
17 Tweed   18 *Combe*   19 *Truro*   20 Broad

'. . . the book of books, the crown of all literature —
Bradshaw's Railway Guide.'

Railways in film and fiction
1 Great Northern & Southern Railway   2 Keighley &
Worth Valley Railway   3 Carnforth   4 Nene Valley Railway
5 *The Importance of Being Earnest* (Oscar Wilde)   6 The
Forth Bridge   7 L&MR 0-4-2 *Lion*   8 *Through the
Looking Glass* (Lewis Carroll)   9 London-Glasgow
10 *Paddington*   11 Adlestrop (Edward Thomas)   12 (*The
Great*) *St Trinian's* (*Train Robbery*)   13 1963, Linslade,
Bucks   14 Rugby   15 William Porter (Will Hay in *Oh, Mr
Porter!*)   16 Copenhagen Tunnels, King's Cross   17 Kyle
of Lochalsh   18 *The Jewel in the Crown*   19 William
Wordsworth   20 The Moretonhampstead branch

Crossword No 7: Facts and figures
Across: 1 151   3 126   5 25   6 779   7 2-4-0   9 113
11 0-8-0   13 '58'   14 46229   17 14   18 2-6-4   19 22
20 '45'   21 60012   22 13   23 75   24 2-8-0   25 76
27 87010   30 '08'   32 600   34 505   35 4-6-0   36 393
37 12   38 790   39 250
Down: 1 1915   2 173   3 1966   4 6202   5 200   8 30453
10 1825   12 81   14 44658   15 26000   16 92220
20 44767   22 1000   26 60   28 7007   29 10:30   31 8500
33 0-4-2   34 532

The Big Four II: LNER
1 GCR ('Forward')   2 0-6-0   3 William Whitelaw
(Viscount Penrith), grandson of William Whitelaw, LNER

Chairman 1923-38 **4** NE **5** Beyer-Garratt 2-8-8-2
6 'B17' 4-6-0 **7** 10000 **8** They were articulated, coach ends sharing a common single bogie. Thus five coaches used only six bogies **9** To be switched on in tunnels when radio reception was lost, so keeping the programme continuous! **10** The Pathe cinema car, showing newsreels, cartoons etc. **11** *Sir Nigel Gresley* **12** The 'Green Arrow' LNER express parcels scheme **13** A 'land cruise' train, a self-contained 'hotel' on wheels travelling from London around Scotland and return **14** Peterborough
15 Whitemoor (March, Cambs) **16** Newcastle Central
17 Meals were served at every seat **18** Racehorses **19** O. V. S. Bulleid (Southern Railway) **20** The 'Master Cutler'

Deltic dilemma
The Duke of Wellington's Regiment, Gordon Highlander, The Green Howards, The Black Watch, Royal Scots Grey, Saint (St) Paddy, Pinza, Nimbus

Picture the scene: St Neots
1 2 million miles since introduction in 1961 **2** Two prominent white spots on a black background **3** They began to receive new numbers in the 55001-22 series
4 Racehorses **5** Finsbury Park, Gateshead, Edinburgh
6 Welwyn — for the viaducts and two tunnels **7** 'Banner repeater' — it repeats the aspect of a signal the sighting of which is obstructed (in this case by the footbridge on which I was standing) **8** Dark blue with white lettering **9** 100 mph speed restriction sign **10** 1981

Speed curve
1 *Silver (Fox)* **2** 'Atbara' **3** *Ionic* **4** 'Castle' (*Drysllwyn Castle*) **5** Didcot **6** *Tresco* **7** Tennant **8** *Elizabeth*
9 *Hardwicke* **10** Duddington **11** *City of Truro*
12 'Dunalastair' **13** 'Atlantic Coast (Express') **14** Sir Daniel Gooch

'Race to the North'

125
Craigentinny (43100); *Bounds Green* (43057); *Neville Hill* (43049); *Yorkshire Post* (43194); *Top of the Pops* (43002); *BBC Points West* (43124)

Twenty questions
1 Patrick Stirling **2** Hotel Great Central **3** Standedge
4 LMS **5** 842 **6** 'Obstruction danger' **7** Owen Glendower **8** Nene Valley Railway, Peterborough
9 Waterloo **10** The Cornish Riviera Express **11** Tay Bridge
12 Vale of Rheidol Light Railway **13** *Oliver Cromwell*
14 *Blucher* **15** Settle & Carlisle, Hellifield to Garsdale
16 Railway Clearing House **17** HTV West **18** Liverpool Street
19 Ministry of Transport **20** M&GN, Bourne-Spalding

Crossword No 8
Across: **1** Princes **5** St Enoch **8** Regulator **9** Custom
12 Dee **13** Dolly **16** *Bonny* **17** Grouping
20 *Yeomanry* **21** Irish **24** Mucky **25** One **26** School
29 Generator **30** Clinker **31** Central (GCR)
Down: **2** *Ingleborough* **3** Caledonian **4** Settle **5** Sir
6 Ness **7** Co-Bo **8** Ryde **10** Train-spotter **11** *Mungo*
14 York **15** Surrey Iron **19** Sykes **18** Tram **22** Scenic
23 (*The Great*) Bear **27** Coal **28** Oban **29** GNR

The National Collection
1 LNER, York, 1927 **2** Swindon **3** Catering vehicles; the centenary of railway catering **4** SR-built 'Merchant Navy', *Ellerman Lines* (35029) **5** It was horse-drawn
6 Sutherland **7** A TPO (Travelling Post Office)
8 Pullman parlour car **9** Queen Adelaide
10 'Coppernob' **11** *Iron Duke* **12** 'Atlantic' (4-4-2)

13 In the Science Museum, London **14** Butlins
15 Woodhead **16** China **17** Signalling — it is an early foot-operated mechanism for signal operation **18** Great Central Railway, Loughborough **19** 'Races to the North'
20 'Deltic', the prototype, in the Science Museum, London

Rocket 150
1 Timothy Hackworth **2** She was found to be over the stipulated 4½ ton weight limit **3** 1838 **4** 50 psi
5 'Coal tanks' **6** Dinting Railway Centre **7** 'Spinners'
8 S. W. Johnson **9** *Earl Bathurst* **10** The Great Western Society **11** Tonbridge-Hastings **12** Three **13** 104 mph
14 Valve gear, from Bulleid to Walschaerts **15** It was the 100th Gresley 'Pacific' to be built **16** 60007 **17** Class '52' **18** Desert Sand, Golden Ochre, Brunswick Green
19 12 **20** 4 hrs 10 mins

Crossword No 9
Across: **1** Derby **4** Kirtley **7** Eye **9** Yate **11** Cleeve
12 *Energy* **13** Yard **14** *Total* **17** Pass **18** Epsom
20 *Merlin* **21** Gricer **22** Diner **24** RHDR (Romney, Hythe & Dymchurch Railway) **25** Leads **28** SECR **29** Albert
30 Sander **31** Open **33** CME **34** General **35** Royal
Down: **1** Didcot **2** *Robert* (*Burns*) **3** Yeovil **4** Key
5 Tweed **6** *Enterprise* **8** High speed **10** Adams
15 Oxenholme **16** *Auld Reekie* **18** End **19** Mgr (Merry-go-round) **23** Niche **25** 'Leader' **26** Audley **27** Scroll
28 Stoke **32** NCL (National Carriers Ltd)

Picture the scene: The Menai Bridge
1 Boys looking for birds' nests accidentally set fire to the timber lining of the tubes **2** Chester & Holyhead Railway **3** Thomas Telford **4** Conway **5** The Admiralty would only allow one pier (on Britannia Rock) so as not to impede navigation **6** I. K. Brunel **7** Robert Stephenson
8 Britannia Tubular Bridge **9** Stone lions **10** A roadway

Bridges . . .
1 Built in 1825, it is the first substantial metal railway bridge ever constructed **2** Midland Railway **3** Meldon
4 It was the first all-concrete viaduct **5** They all cross the Anglo-Scottish border **6** 82 **7** Maidenhead, on the Thames **8** Ouse Viaduct, Balcombe **9** A knighthood
10 The Tay Bridge (they were the section that collapsed)
11 Welwyn, Herts **12** West Highland Extension Railway, near Tyndrum **13** Road over canal over railway **14** Swing bridge **15** Barmouth bridge **16** Spanning Sonning cutting **17** Nidd **Picture question 1:** The Severn Bridge
Picture question 2: Prince Albert

. . . and Tunnels
1 Between Folkestone and Dover, SECR **2** Glasgow Queen Street **3** Canal (Thames & Medway) **4** Electric power cables **5** Standedge **6** Severn **7** Summit **8** Bramhope
9 Blea Moor **10** Clayton **11** Northern Line **12** The Greathead shield, to aid boring and lining tunnels through soft material **13** Shugborough **14** 4-2 double-track on the main line, 2 single-track on the Watford local electric line **15** Between Dawlish and Teignmouth, GWR South Devon line **16** The Somerset & Dorset **17** Great Central Railway **18** The 'Thames Clyde Express' (35 tunnels, six over a mile long) **19** Nottingham Victoria **Picture question:** West — the east (London) end portal is completely plain

From the train
The Forth Bridge; between Dawlish and Teignmouth; outside St Pancras

Inclines
1 Shap **2** The 'Long Drag' **3** Lickey (the BR number of

MR No 2290, 'Big Bertha') 4 Beattock 5 1 in 36, Dainton 6 Baxenden 7 Bincombe (Weymouth-Dorchester) 8 Masbury 9 Ilfracombe 10 Dove Holes 11 Rattery 12 Whitrope, Waverley route, northbound 13 Euston 14 Manchester Victoria 15 Cobbinshaw 16 Callendar & Oban line, Caledonian Railway 17 Woodhead 18 1 in 100 19 1988 (May 15 — two Class '37s' banked a Class '47' on a West Country-Edinburgh and Glasgow sleeper) **Picture question:** Corrour

The Settle & Carlisle
1 Garsdale 2 Dent Head 3 Batty Moss viaduct 4 None — it is a dry valley 5 River Eden 6 NER 7 Dent 8 Bishop Eric Treacy, the 'Railway Bishop', who died suddenly on the platform while photographing trains in May 1978 9 Navvy villages 10 To prevent engines being uncontrollably spun round by high winds, as happened on several occasions 11 Shotlock Hill 12 The peat bog swallowed up 50,000 cu yds of material before it was decided that an embankment would be impossible 13 Smardale 14 Lazonby & Kirkoswald 15 Cumbria 16 1970 17 Low House Crossing signal box and level crossing 18 A viaduct 19 Ten (Easter 1978) **Picture question 1:** Hawes Junction **Picture question 2:** It is the highest English main-line station

Gradient profile
1 Woodhead 2 Masbury 3 Corrour 4 Tyndrum 5 Dainton 6 Beattock 7 Rannoch 8 Evershot 9 Whitrope 10 Rattery

Drumochter

More marshalling
4, 10, 6, 9, 1, 3, 2, 8, 5, 7

Points, North British, railcar, auto-train, diesel-electric, power box, signal post, first class, *Evening Star*, Saint Pancras, Paddington

Crossword No 10
Across: 1 Camden 4 Bank 6 NCC (Northern Counties Committee) 8 Silver (*Fox* and 'Jubilee') 10 Syston 11 Narrow 12 *Lion* 13 Inside 14 Welwyn 15 SECR 16 Gauge 17 Inn 18 *Anzac* 21 Disc 24 Raunds 25 *Active* 26 Plum 27 'Single' 29 Tablet 31 Edward 32 CME (Chief Mechanical Engineer) 33 Edis 34 Severn
Down: 1 Castles ('Castle' Class) 2 Melton Constable 3 Eden 4 Barrow-in-Furness 5 Key 6 Notting Hill Gate 7 Connel 9 Raven 10 Swing 19 Crest 20 Edale 22 Campden 23 'Baltic' 28 Edge 30 Exe

Mixed goods
1 Andover — others are names of SR 'West Country' Class locos 2 South Eastern — others were prefixed by 'London & . . .' 3 Foregate Street — others are Birmingham stations 4 *Duchess of Hamilton* — others were rescued from Barry scrapyard 5 Churchward — others gave their names to valve gears 6 Hawksworth — others were Georges 7 'A1s' — they were Thompson/Peppercorn locos, the others were Gresley's 8 Stanmore — others are termini on the Metropolitan Line 9 Wye — others are 'Valley' preserved lines 10 Frederick — others are 'Fort' termini in Scotland 11 Bulleid — others were knighted 12 Junction — which was Grand, while the others were 'Great' 13 Lord Nelson — Southern Railway, while the others were LNWR classes 14 Yorkshire — others form the name of the MS&LR, predecessor of the GCR 15 Afternoon — others preceded *Star* in loco names 16 Cornish Riviera — others were names of trains and individual locomotives 17 Ullswater — other lakes were

served by railway stations 18 Cambrian — its title was Railways, while the others were singular 19 Royal Border Bridge — a stone-faced brick viaduct, the others being metal bridges 20 *Titanic* — others were ships after which Class '40s' were named

The stately homes of England
1 Castle 2 Hall 3 Abbey — the 'red herring' 4 Manor 5 Manor 6 Hall 7 Manor 8 Hall 9 Grange 10 Hall and Castle

The preservation scene II
1 'Jubilee' No 5596 *Bahamas* 2 George Stephenson 3 It was the only 'Black Five' built with the Stephenson link-motion valve gear 4 Keighley & Worth Valley 5 Clapham, South London 6 The Middleton Railway, Leeds 7 Whisky distillery 8 West Somerset Railway 9 The Kent & East Sussex Railway 10 Bowater's paper mill 11 H. P. Bulmer (Bulmer's Railway Centre, Hereford) 12 Quainton Railway Society 13 Association of Railway Preservation Societies 14 'Great Little Trains of Wales' 15 To avoid the risk of fire from cinders in the densely forested areas beside the line 16 Cambrian Railways 17 Ravenglass & Eskdale Railway 18 Alan Pegler 19 Haworth **Picture question:** M&GNR; North Norfolk Railway

Barry
1 1962 2 It was the first of the Barry locomotives to be bought and preserved 3 It became derailed, sustained minor damage and was withdrawn on the spot to be condemned with the other locomotives 4 Robert Adley 5 'B1' 4-6-0 No 61264 6 Somerset & Dorset line 7 Bath (Green Park) 8 West Somerset Railway 9 C. B. Collett 10 250 psi 11 The route availability of the 'Kings' excluded their use on the GWR lines west of Cardiff, so the locomotives were unable to travel to Briton Ferry 12 Seven 13 Liverpool; Lime Street

The Big Four III: GWR
1 Taff Vale Railway 2 Hammersmith & City Railway 3 Slough-Oxford 4 Streamlining 5 Camping coaches 6 Across Saltash Bridge 7 Westbury 8 No 4073 *Caerphilly Castle* 9 The pioneer British 'Pacific' *The Great Bear* 10 *King George V* 11 Cogload 12 Brunel's timber viaducts 13 The 'Cheltenham Spa Express' (the 'Cheltenham Flyer') 14 One 15 Docks 16 St Ives, Cornwall 17 The handing over of the first American-built locomotive to enter service with a British railway company during the Second World War 18 Stanier 2-8-0 19 A Spitfire 20 Viscount Portal 21 William Heath Robinson

Down express
1 St Pancras 2 Manchester 3 Speedfreight 4 Cathedrals 5 'Bristolian' 6 'Pines Express' 7 'Dragon' 8 Two-hour 9 'Ocean' 10 'Clansman'

Paddington, Cheltenham (the 'Cheltenham Flyer')

Slip coaches II
1 'Stanhope' 2 *Highflyer* 3 Caledonian 4 Worsdell 5 Peppercorn 6 *Cleeve* 7 Rose Grove 8 *Africa* 9 Tonbridge 10 Inter-City 11 Thomas 12 Furness 13 Stroudley 14 Frobisher 15 Rushey Platt 16 Leamington 17 Inverurie 18 Pullman cars 19 Pannier 20 High speed

'The operation of slipping is performed by means of a lever by a Slip Guard . . .'

Crossword No 11
Across: 1 Teak 7 Dairycoates 8 Exeter 9 Snow Hill

11 Top 12 Hat 14 *Anzac* 17 Aviemore 20 Poem
21 *Lady* 23 *Tasmania* 27 Orchy 28 Red 29 Yat
30 *Defiance* 32 Sloane 33 *Scafell Pike* 34 Edit
Down: 1 Trent Valley 2 Adelphi 3 Par 4 Iron
5 Gothic 6 Bell 7 Denham 9 'Star' 10 Loco
13 Compartment 15 Neath 16 Arms 18 Ely 19 Over
20 PLA (Port of London Authority) 22 Dyce 24 Ayre
25 Middle 26 Neyland 27 *Oliver* (*Cromwell*, preserved
at Bressingham) 30 'Duck' 31 Copy 32 Sky

Picture the scene: In the box
1 'Normal', 'Line clear', 'Train on line' 2 Facing point
lock 3 WRONG 4 Black 5 Right-hand end
6 Detonator placer for the down line (for the up line the
chevrons would point upwards) 7 A 'pegger' has a
commutator handle to enable the signalman to operate the
instrument; a 'non-pegger' repeats the indication of a
block instrument in the neighbouring box 8 350 yards
9 440 yards (¼ mile) 10 4 bells consecutively

Junction boxes
1 Bromley 2 Clapham 3 Shalford 4 Belvoir 5 Aller
6 Torquay 7 Verney 8 Norwood 9 Hooton 10 Canal
11 Midland 12 Sheet 13 Spean 14 Lansdown 15 Retford

Cheltenham Spa Malvern Road East (Signal Box)

Lever leads I
1 Starter 2 Line clear 3 Intermediate 4 Kinnaber
5 Trap 6 Crossover 7 Advanced 8 Gantry
9 Pegger 10 Distant 11 Northallerton 12 Off

1 = SIGNAL 2 = POINTS 3 = LOCK 4 = DISC

Junctions
1 Bulleid, bullhead 2 'Pines', *Pinza* 3 Marsh, Marples
4 Stephens, *Stepney* 5 Bradshaw, Bradford

Change for . . .?
1 Bletchley 2 Hitchin 3 Settle Junction 4 Connel Ferry
5 Didcot 6 Evercreech Junction 7 Three Bridges

Empty stock II
Across: 2 Abbot 6 Gear 7 High 8 Air 9 Oak
10 Snow 12 East 14 Disc 18 Shap 20 *Aim* 21 End
22 Blea 23 Leek 24 Royal
Down: 1 Seven 2 'Arrow' 3 Brake 4 Three 5 *Agnes*
11 O.V.S. 13 Ash 15 *Ingle* 16 Clear 17 *Paddy*
18 Small 19 Abbey

People
1 Herbert 2 Sir Robert McAlpine 3 Armstrong 4 89
5 The shock following the collapse of his Tay Bridge
6 G. J. Churchward 7 Sir Gilbert Claughton, LNWR
Chairman 1911-21 8 Brothers 9 Great Central
10 London Underground Railway 11 George Hudson
12 ICI 13 Sir Felix Pole 14 John Farmer 15 W. R. Sykes
16 American 17 Thomas Brassey 18 Barbara Castle
19 I. K. Brunel 20 Minister of Transport

Crossword No 12
Across: 2 *Tehran* 7 Urie 8 Slough 9 *Abercorn*
10 Spur 12 Deeley 14 Street 15 Eye 16 Holland
19 Rye 21 Act 22 Ballast 26 Wye 28 Eleven 29 *Iseult*
32 Bolt 33 *Hamilton* 35 *Rocket* 36 Nest 37 Spring
Down: 1 'Crab' 2 'Terrier' 3 Haworth 4 Arundel
5 Worse 6 Charwelton 8 Skye 11 Pye 13 Lune
14 Shrewsbury 17 Oil 18 LMS 20 Lane 23 Althorp
24 Termini 25 Selling 27 Eil 30 Stoke 31 Unit
34 Ouse

What's in a name?
'Castle' Class (GWR); 'County' Class (GWR); 'Merchant
Navy' Class (SR); 'West Country' Class (SR); 'Battle of
Britain' Class (SR); Class '40' diesel-electric (BR)

Headboards
1 'Red Dragon' 2 'Bristolian' 3 'Flying' 4 'Golden
Arrow' 5 Cutler 6 'Talisman' 7 'Thames-Clyde'
8 'Coronation' 9 'Atlantic Coast (Express')

'Royal Scot'; Edinburgh, Glasgow

Why?
1 Early signalmen were policemen 2 To protest
unsuccessfully against the closure of the line (the London-
bound train was the last to run) 3 GWR up trains were
running eastwards, SR trains westwards towards Exeter
Central and the LSWR main line to Waterloo 4 The
station was named after the local landowner and railway
promoter, Sir Harry Verney 5 To use for snow clearance
during the very bad winter of 1946-7 6 The Headmaster
of Uppingham School objected to the use of the school's
name on a locomotive 7 It was named after a local public
house frequented by shepherds 8 The conversion from
broad to standard gauge left the distance between the
tracks wider than normal 9 After nearby Crewe Hall,
there already being a Coppenhall station on the Grand
Junction Railway 10 It was a joint line so it was not
originally covered by the 1921 Railways Act (neither were
the CLC and S&DJR) 11 It was named after Waterloo
Bridge across the Thames, opened in 1817, two years after
the battle 12 It was at Oswestry in England

Picture the scene: King's Cross approaches
1 Gasworks Tunnels 2 Copenhagen Tunnels 3 The
Regent's Canal section of the Grand Union Canal 4 Belle
Isle 5 North London Railway 6 The 40th anniversary of
the first public non-stop run to Edinburgh 7 1978
8 Peterborough 9 Royston

West Coast, East Coast
Up lines: 2 Alloa, APT, Trent, Tondu 4 Level, Liss,
staff, Fort 6 *Isles*, set, Town, Norton 8 Iron, Neville, ED,
Dent, TI 10 Vale, Eye, Eden, North, HNG 12 Relief,
fast, Tan, NEC, CLC 14 Ebbw, Willows, shot, TPO
16 Sand, Dee, *Esk*, Keymer, RLS (Robert Louis Stevenson)
Down lines: 1 Earls, slip, Percy, Yarm 3 Saltash, Hest,
Travel 5 Off, Fife, extra, *Aim*, MSJA 7 Key, York,
Kendal, Lairg 9 NH, HM, 'Mogul', length, horn
11 Seaham, Midland, Dove 13 Red Star, Rye, Eastern
15 Sam Fay, yard, Didcot, TS

Mallaig, Inverness
Carlisle, Tyneside
Preston, Leeds, York
Stafford, Grantham
Euston, King's Cross

Crossword No 13
Across: 1 Sheffield 5 Belah 7 Napier 8 Brill 10 Bat
11 Lever 13 Arch 15 Holyhead 17 Oban 18 Span
21 *Drake* 22 Pies 25 Gear 26 *Minstrel* 29 Ryde
30 Blake 32 BRB (British Railways Board) 33 *Eagle*
34 Stoves 36 Level 37 Edmondson
Down: 1 *Syn* 2 Esplanade 3 *French* 4 Dart 5 Ball
6 *Alberta* 8 'Baby' 9 Leads 12 Scoop 14 Holden
16 *Exeter* 19 Preserves 20 North 23 Incline 24 Smoke
27 Tare 28 Lynton 31 Earl 32 Blue 35 *Sun*

Central Line
1 James 2 Green 3 Hatch 4 North 5 Cross 6 Upton
7 Docks 8 Colin 9 White 10 Acton 11 Chalk 12 Manor

Metropolitan

Pantographs

1 down left *Round*   1 down right *Royal*   2 up *Thane*   2 down *Times*   3 down *Darby*   4 up *Bruce*   4 down *Burns*   5 down *Lowry*   6 down *Witch*   7 down *Peter*   8 down *Stoke*   9 down *Ellis*   10 up *Henry*   10 down *Hallé*   11 down *Isles*   12 up *Airey*   12 down *André*

Sign on

1 'Rule 55 exempt' — track circuits or other detectors are provided so a member of the train crew need not go to the signal box as instructed in Rule 55 to report his train stationary at the signal so marked   2 Termination of a temporary speed restriction   3 Plunger or telephone provided at signal   4 Automatic signal   5 Telephone box   6 Old-style warning board in advance of speed restriction, with maximum speed given in figures   7 Milepost, '¾'   8 Permanent speed restriction

Ten years on

1 Ray Buckton   2 Bedford   3 The 125th anniversary of Paddington station   4 A hot axle-box   5 Penmanshiel tunnel, between Berwick and Dunbar, collapsed   6 Paisley   7 Jubilee Line   8 Rail Riders   9 £10   10 Near Northallerton   11 Kensington Gardens, near the Albert Memorial   12 Stevenage and Peterborough   13 The 'Centenary Express'   14 London (King's Cross) and Leeds   15 Harold Macmillan; Blackpool, for the Conservative Party Conference   16 Western Region, Paddington, Plymouth, Penzance   17 Invergowrie   18 222 Marylebone Road   19 155 mph   20 A ban on the carrying of bicycles during peak hours

The long and the tall

Shrewsbury; Exeter Middle (Exeter St Davids); Totnes

Lever leads II

1 Kemble   2 Dalston   3 Evercreech   4 Georgemas   5 Over   6 Watford   7 Ebbw   8 Yarwell   9 Uphill   10 Red Posts   11 Cowley Bridge   12 Bopeep

1 = YORK   2 = CREWE   3 = DERBY   4 = RUGBY

Colloquially speaking

1 To create a vacuum in the train brake pipe   2 Semaphore signal arm   3 2-8-0 wheel arrangement   4 Space between the rails of an individual track   5 Space between adjacent tracks   6 The Lancashire & Yorkshire Railway   7 Of an engineman, travelling in the train, rather than on the footplate   8 Signal   9 Overheated axle-box   10 Ground signal

Crossword No 14

Across: 5 (The) Lawn   8 Railfreight   9 Pit   10 Abingdon   12 Edge   15 Starter   18 Elton   19 *Ellis*   20 Leeds   21 Erith   23 Horse   24 *Eagle*   26 Rainham   28 Ryde   30 Fire-bars   32 *Irt*   33 Bricklayer's   34 Kent   **Down:** 1 Rabbit   2 'Clan'   3 Lion   4 Shoe   6 Aspect (Multiple aspect signalling)   7 Nottingham   11 Gateshead   13 Dieselise   14 Walker   15 *Silver Link*   16 Awe   17 Regret   22 Ich   25 Gorton   27 *Aurora*   29 *Earl*   30 Face   31 Bays

Arms and liveries

Across: 1 Cream   2 Madonna   3 Knot ('Knotty')   4 Tudor   5 Royal   6 Great Central   7 Bristol   8 Lining   9 GNR   10 Canterbury   11 York   12 Stars   13 Silver ('Silver Jubilee')   14 Rail   **Down:** 15 Hull   16 London   17 North Stafford   18 Wyvern   19 North Eastern   20 NBR   21 Rose   22 Lincoln   23 Norwich   24 Horse   25 Engine

The Big Four IV: Southern Railway

1 It was chain-driven   2 Sir Nigel Gresley, LNER   3 'Air-smoothed'   4 'Q1' Class 'Austerity' 0-6-0   5 'Schools'   6 The 'Golden Arrow'   7 There were 8 beats per revolution of the driving wheels   8 The 'Devon Belle'   9 Shunting engines ('USA' Class 0-6-0T Nos 30061-74)   10 1933   11 They were the only electric multiple-unit Pullman trains in the world   12 Its new 'modern image' stations, such as the celebrated example at Surbiton   13 It was overhead AC, not third rail DC   14 Public Relations   15 The Lynton & Barnstaple Railway   16 The SR did not lay down water troughs   17 Diesel electric 1-Co-Co-1 locomotives   18 Nine   19 The two separate SE&CR and LB&SCR stations were knocked into one, and the platforms numbered 1-17 in sequence across both stations   20 Sir Eustace Missenden

Additional service

21 + 1938 + 1890 + 532 + 91 = 4472 (*Flying Scotsman*)

Waterloo departure

1 Wadebridge   2 Alresford   3 Templecombe   4 Eastleigh   5 Richmond   6 Litchfield   7 Ottery   8 Okehampton

Pullman predicament

Adrian, Agatha, Amber, Argus, Aries, Athene, Aurelia, Avon, Carina, Cecilia, Eagle, Emerald, Garnet, Hawk, Hercules, Heron, Iolanthe, Irene, Isle of Thanet, Joan, Juana, Lucille, Magpie, Opal, Orion, Pearl, Pegasus Bar, Perseus, Raven, Robin, Rosemary, Sappho, Sheila, Thrush, Wren, Zena, Zenobia

Picture the scene: Wylam

1 1838   2 The North Eastern Railway   3 William Hedley   4 Short for 'diligence', a type of continental horse-drawn stage-coach   5 *Puffing Billy*   6 Oak, with renewable beech surface strips   7 George Stephenson   8 Timothy Hackworth   9 The centre light   10 If a train is detained, the Guard, Shunter or Fireman must go to the signal box and remind the signalman of the presence of the train.

Early signalling

1 Green   2 GWR   3 The time-interval system, where a line was considered blocked for a certain time after a train had passed, then was considered clear   4 The London & Croydon Railway   5 Gosport   6 Prof Wheatstone   7 Abbot's Ripton   8 'Somersault' centre-pivoted signals   9 Track circuiting   10 A 'fish tail' notch was cut out to distinguish them from stop signals

Crossword No 15

Across: 2 Westinghouse   7 Dome   8 *ABC*   9 Stow   10 Beaver   11 Eye   12 Keith   13 Port   15 Slot   17 *Trevone*   18 Mint   20 *Anti*   22 Offices   24 Isle   26 *Mars*   29 Largs   31 Gas   32 *Packet*   33 *Tiny*   34 Ide   35 Race (to the North)   36 Mangotsfield   **Down:** 1 Bopeep   2 Weaver   3 'Shark'   4 Incline   5 Upwell   6 Eccentric   9 'Schools'   14 *Own*   15 Sea   16 Immingham   17 Tuffley   19 Toe   21 NBR   23 Cardiff   25 Listen   27 *Accord*   28 Speech   30 Speke

End of the line

1 Portpatrick   2 Aylesbury   3 Newport Pagnell   4 Swanage   5 Llandudno   6 Macduff   7 Brill   8 Thurso   9 CLC (Cheshire Lines Committee)   10 Highworth   11 Withernsea   12 Central   13 St Ives   14 Ballachulish

Kyle of Lochalsh

The last word

1 Broad gauge   2 Uxbridge   3 Falmouth   4 Fowler   5 *Evening Star*   6 Raven   7 Swindon   8 Tail lamp   9 Observation car   10 Penzance

Buffer stop